A Dog Show COMPANION

THE ULTIMATE
Dog Show Record Book,
Planner, and Guide to Help
You Succeed in the Ring!

By

LEILA GRANDEMANGE

ISBN 978-0-9975658-6-7

First printing May 4, 2021

DREAMING BIG

REQUIRES US TO

RISE TO THE CHALLENGE

AND

REACH FOR THE STARS

IN ORDER TO

REALIZE OUR DREAMS!

~ Leila Grandemange

Table of Contents

A dog show, also called a "conformation show," is a competitive dog sport designed to display purebred dogs to be judged for conformity to their respective breed standards. Competing in conformation is hard work, but also lots of fun! As you prepare for the big day in the ring, you'll develop a close bond with your dog, meet other exhibitors, and learn tips to help you succeed. Along the way, you'll want to stay organized and continue learning. This book was written to help you record your journey, rise to the challenge, and realize your dog show dreams, while creating a treasured keepsake of the dogs you love. It's the perfect motivational companion for your dog show adventures! There are five parts:

Note: This book is specific to conformation shows with the American Kennel Club (AKC) but can benefit those who compete with other organizations. Check periodically for the latest updates with your organization, as things in the dog world can change.

PART I: QUICK REFERENCE

- **2-Year Show Calendar:** Plan and record dates of upcoming shows and dog-related events, such as handling classes and health clinics. Track your girls' heat cycles to plan for future shows, and jot down your goals to help you stay on track.

- **Show Team Hub:** Log the names of your canine competitors, along with pertinent information needed to fill out show entries—i.e., date of birth, registration number, sire x dam. There is space for 12 dogs.

PART II: DOG SHOW COMPETITION LOG: 100 CHARTS (refer to sample entry on page 5)

- **Enter a show:** This section begins with practical information to help you find and enter a dog show.

- **Record the current point schedule** of your show's division for quick reference in the charts provided.

- **Build confidence with positive affirmations** before each event. Craft your own affirmations using the provided tips, and jot them down in the designated area on your dog show log alongside your goals. Recite your affirmation regularly in the lead-up to the show to nurture a winning mindset.

- **Track your dog(s) show career** with 100 competition charts. Log placements, points, and insights: What went well? What needs improvement? Thoughts on the judging, show venue, etc.? Also, record fees, hotel stays, goals, and more—refer to the sample entry. AKC award abbreviations are explained on page 172.

PART III: SHOW TALK AND TIPS

- Walk through a show from a brief history to Best in Show! Plus, fine-tune your craft with pre-show and showtime tips on goal setting, grooming, ring presentation, wardrobe, a winning mindset, and more.

- As you dive into this book, I suggest printing out the goal worksheet (found on page 165) to kickstart your goal-setting process.

PART IV: ESSENTIAL DOG SHOW RESOURCES

- Discover a handy guide to dog show essentials, including show gear, point counting, dog parts & movement terms, pet sitter form, and a comprehensive resource section with online links and more.

PART V: A-Z DOG SHOW JUDGE LOG AND CONTACTS

- Record the names of judges you've shown to and which dogs were presented, names of handlers, etc. Part 5 ends with space for your vital emergency contacts, such as your veterinarian and pet sitter.

Sample Dog Show Competition Log

SHOW DATE	NAME OF DOG/ARM BAND NUMBER	EVENT TYPE	NAME OF SHOW
Aug. 10 2022	Joyful Sir William, "Willy" 22	AKC Conformation	Fork Ridge K.C. Greensboro N.C.

CLASS ENTERED	PLACE IN CLASS	ENTRY IN CLASS	TOTAL ENTRY	POINTS	AWARD	GROUP	BEST IN SHOW
BBE Bred by Exhibitor	1	3	20	4pt MAJOR	BOB	4	

ENTRY BREAK DOWN * 7-8-3-2 RING # 4 TIME 10:30 BREEDS BEFORE Maltese

BREED JUDGE Mrs. Vivian Sylvester GROUP Dr. Todd Given BIS _____

AWARDS TODAY WD, BOW, BOB, BBBE, Toy Group 4.

POINTS COMING IN SHOW 11 POINTS EARNED TODAY 4 POINTS TO DATE 15

OTHER RESULTS/JUDGES (I.E. NOHS) Owner Handled Best of Breed.

Best Bred by Exhibitor Group 2. Judge J. Steele

NEW TITLE New AKC Champion! Woohoo!

COMMENTS AND TAKE-AWAYS

What went well: We did a great up and back. Willy kept a straight line and wagged the entire time! Things to improve: Keep working on his free stack.

Judging: Friendly judge, very encouraging. Commented on Willy's sweet expression.

Venue: Clean, well organized. Gotta come back!

SHOW PREPARATIONS AND FEES

SHOW ADDRESS/ETA Approx. 5 hrs, 30th St. Greensboro N.C.

SHOW PHOTO TAKEN [YES ✓] [NO] PHOTO SENT TO JUDGE [YES ✓] [NO] PHOTOGRAPHER _____

FEES: ENTRY $30 PHOTOS $35 PARKING $5 GROOMING _____ HEALTH CLINICS $50

HANDLER NAME/FEE _____ HEALTH CLINIC TIMES OFA heart clinic 9 AM

HOTEL _____ PET SITTER _____

THINGS TO REMEMBER Bring the new liver treats, folding chairs

TODAY'S GOAL Help Willy stay happy, relaxed, and wagging in the ring.

POSITIVE AFFIRMATION I am mentally strong and perform well under pressure.

* Means 7 class males, 8 class females, 3 male champions, 2 female champions are entered. Only count dogs present to tally points.

Introduction

From Dancing to Dogs to Why I Wrote This Book

Who would have thought that holding a winning ribbon at a dog show could bring a person so much joy! But there I was, at my first show, holding the winning ribbon, grinning from ear to ear with my husband and kids. So how did I get here? Funny enough, my dog show journey began in a ballet studio at the tender age of 7. I also had a beautiful Springer Spaniel during these early years, who would become my absolute best friend growing up, always offering me comfort and joy.

Fast forward to my twenties, a dream come true! I was accepted into a ballet company. But I didn't stay there long. I soon met my husband, who whisked me off to France. That was where I met the Cavalier King Charles Spaniel and instantly fell in love. Of course, now, I had to have one of my own. But I didn't just want any puppy. I wanted a graceful dance partner to waltz me around the ring. And so the search began. That's how I ended up with our first Cavalier King Charles Spaniel show puppy!

Dog show beginnings . . .

After returning to America, I eagerly dove into the dog show world. I registered my dogs, read books on dog showing, joined handling classes and the breed club, took notes, and learned on the go. The long-awaited day arrived. It was showtime! The morning of the show, butterflies came in droves, upsetting my tummy. But I told myself, "This is just another stage. Plus, I have an amazing partner!" Looking back, it's all a bit of a blur. I know I made mistakes in the ring, but the judge was super sweet, and my dog was happy and attentive. To my delight and surprise, he won and earned his first points! That dog was my first dog show dance partner, patiently enduring my newbie "owner-handler" mistakes while wagging his way to his AKC Champion title. I'll always treasure the memories of training, traveling to shows, and creating a close bond with my dog. That bond would later become key to achieving my "owner-handler" dog show dreams.

A few years later, I decided to start breeding my Cavalier King Charles Spaniels. Once I was faced with choosing show puppies and deciding which would continue in my breeding program, conformation shows took on a new dimension, and the true purpose of the sport hit home. So what is the true purpose, and how does it influence all we do as dog fanciers, exhibitors, judges, and breeders?

The true purpose of the sport . . .

Although many exhibitors show dogs just for fun, as I did for a season, the original purpose of Conformation Shows is to evaluate breeding stock. The American Kennel Club (AKC) writes, "The dog's conformation, overall appearance and structure is an indication of the dog's ability to produce quality purebred puppies. This is what is supposed to be judged in the ring. While a dog show may look like a breed beauty pageant, actually it's not supposed to be. Dogs are to be measured by how closely they conform to the Breed Standard. The closer a dog's appearance is to the breed's standard, the better that dog's ability will be to produce puppies that meet that breed standard. It's also the reason why mixed breeds and spayed or neutered purebreds are ineligible to compete in Conformation."

Staying focused on the sport's purpose has helped me put my best paw forward as a breeder-owner-handler. It has also helped me stay motivated, especially when things get rough. Why am I sharing all this? Because as dog show exhibitors and competitors, we're all on a journey, traveling together with a common goal—**it truly takes a village to succeed at showing dogs.** With that in mind, if we aren't sure where we're heading, why we're traveling, or with whom we are sharing the road, it's easy to get sidetracked, discouraged, or call it quits, like the rabbit who ran out of steam in the tale of "The Rabbit and the Turtle."

This brings me to why I wrote this book . . .

Having traveled the dog show journey, experienced its ups and downs, and learned from others, I wanted to give back and offer fellow exhibitors a practical tool to inspire them to start well, stay true to their journey, and finish strong. How will this book help you do that?

This book will help you:

- 🐾 Lay a strong foundation for your dog show journey by highlighting the true purpose of the sport.

- 🐾 Embrace your unique role in the dog show world and feel part of the bigger picture—"The Village."

- 🐾 Prepare for the ring and avoid potential pitfalls with practical pre-show and show-time tips.

- 🐾 Reflect on past wins/losses/training/grooming/judging notes, fine-tune and plan for future shows. This information also gives insight into which dogs to breed on to improve your lines.

- 🐾 Stay goal-oriented and organized campaigning your dogs; map a training plan and see it through.

- 🐾 Plan upcoming shows and remember dog-related goals and "to-do's" using the 2-year show planner.

- 🐾 Recall names of judges you've shown to using the A-Z address book, and which dogs were presented.

- 🐾 Keep a personal journal of achievements and knowledge gained over the years. Then, refer back to it anytime to compare your dog's progress at shows week-to-week, month-to-month, or year-to-year.

- 🐾 Stay motivated, especially in hard times. Returning to your dog show notes can boost your confidence and fuel your journey. You'll see where you started and how far you've come!

- 🐾 Create a winning mindset with positive affirmations to help you build confidence, rise to the challenge, and achieve your dreams.

- 🐾 Gift yourself a precious keepsake of your dog show team—titled or not, each one a champion at heart.

- 🐾 And finally—relax, enjoy the dog show journey, and finish strong!

20 years later . . .

So there you have it, how I went from dancing to dogs to writing this book. I'm grateful that my dog show journey began in a ballet studio. There, I learned that practice, practice, practice makes perfect. I also learned it takes a village to put on a successful show! Now, 20 years after my first dog show, after having bred and shown numerous champions and experienced ups and downs along the road, I can genuinely say— participating in conformation shows while experiencing the camaraderie and community it offers has made me a more well-rounded competitor. It also inspired me to write this book, hoping it will be a valuable and motivational resource for other dog show fanciers. Have fun with it. Realize that you are thoughtfully mapping your journey while creating precious memories with your furry friends.

One last word of encouragement. Don't get too caught up in the points and titles, how many champions you've made up, or embarrassing moments at shows. We all fumble and fall sometimes; we get up, learn, and grow. Thankfully, no matter what happens along our path, we have an extraordinary dance partner to lead us through the twists and turns, lift our spirits when we're down, and shower us with unconditional love. May we always be worthy of such heartfelt doggie devotion.

Wherever you are on your dog show journey, whatever your unique role, event, or goals, I wish you dreams come true and a rainbow of winning ribbons. But mostly, I wish you to cherish your beloved dogs and enjoy your journey—this is where true success awaits with lots of happy tails!

Joyfully yours,
Leila Grandemange

Photos: Dancing around the ring with my beloved dog, and enjoying puppy kisses!

"Sing like no one is listening.
Love like you've never been hurt.
Dance like nobody's watching,
and live like it's heaven on earth!"

~ Willliam Purkey

Part 1
Quick Reference

2-YEAR SHOW CALENDAR

SHOW TEAM HUB

Dogs are not our whole life, but they make our lives whole.
—Roger Caras

January Show Calendar: Year _____

2- YEAR PLANNER

SUN	MON	TUES	WED	THU	FRID	SAT

MY UPCOMING SHOWS AND DOGGIE "TO DO'S"

_____
_____
_____
_____
_____
_____
_____
_____
_____
_____

GOAL ACTION STEPS: _____

_____

January Show Calendar: Year _____

SUN	MON	TUES	WED	THU	FRID	SAT

MY UPCOMING SHOWS AND DOGGIE "TO DO'S"

_____

_____

_____

_____

_____

_____

_____

_____

GOAL ACTION STEPS:

_____

February Show Calendar: Year _____

2- YEAR PLANNER

SUN	MON	TUES	WED	THU	FRID	SAT

MY UPCOMING SHOWS AND DOGGIE "TO DO'S"

_____

_____

_____

_____

_____

_____

_____

_____

_____

_____

GOAL ACTION STEPS: _____

_____

February Show Calendar: Year _____

SUN	MON	TUES	WED	THU	FRID	SAT

MY UPCOMING SHOWS AND DOGGIE "TO DO'S"

_____

_____

_____

_____

_____

_____

_____

_____

_____

GOAL ACTION STEPS: _____

March Show Calendar: Year _____

2- YEAR PLANNER

SUN	MON	TUES	WED	THU	FRID	SAT

MY UPCOMING SHOWS AND DOGGIE "TO DO'S"

_____

_____

_____

_____

_____

_____

_____

_____

_____

GOAL ACTION STEPS:

_____

_____

March Show Calendar: Year _____

SUN	MON	TUES	WED	THU	FRID	SAT

MY UPCOMING SHOWS AND DOGGIE "TO DO'S"

_____

_____

_____

_____

_____

_____

_____

_____

GOAL ACTION STEPS: _____

_____

April Show Calendar: Year _____

2- YEAR PLANNER

SUN	MON	TUES	WED	THU	FRID	SAT

MY UPCOMING SHOWS AND DOGGIE "TO DO'S"

_____

_____

_____

_____

_____

_____

_____

_____

_____

GOAL ACTION STEPS: _____

_____

April Show Calendar: Year _____

SUN	MON	TUES	WED	THU	FRID	SAT
☐	☐	☐	☐	☐	☐	☐
☐	☐	☐	☐	☐	☐	☐
☐	☐	☐	☐	☐	☐	☐
☐	☐	☐	☐	☐	☐	☐
☐	☐	☐	☐	☐	☐	☐

MY UPCOMING SHOWS AND DOGGIE "TO DO'S"

_____

_____

_____

_____

_____

_____

_____

_____

_____

GOAL ACTION STEPS:

_____

May Show Calendar: Year _____

2- YEAR PLANNER

SUN	MON	TUES	WED	THU	FRID	SAT
☐	☐	☐	☐	☐	☐	☐
☐	☐	☐	☐	☐	☐	☐
☐	☐	☐	☐	☐	☐	☐
☐	☐	☐	☐	☐	☐	☐
☐	☐	☐	☐	☐	☐	☐

MY UPCOMING SHOWS AND DOGGIE "TO DO'S"

_____
_____
_____
_____
_____
_____
_____
_____
_____
_____

GOAL ACTION STEPS:

_____
_____

May Show Calendar: Year _____

SUN	MON	TUES	WED	THU	FRID	SAT

MY UPCOMING SHOWS AND DOGGIE "TO DO'S"

_____

_____

_____

_____

_____

_____

_____

_____

GOAL ACTION STEPS:

_____

June Show Calendar: Year _____

2- YEAR PLANNER

SUN	MON	TUES	WED	THU	FRID	SAT

MY UPCOMING SHOWS AND DOGGIE "TO DO'S"

_____

_____

_____

_____

_____

_____

_____

_____

GOAL ACTION STEPS: _____

_____

June Show Calendar: Year _____

SUN	MON	TUES	WED	THU	FRID	SAT

MY UPCOMING SHOWS AND DOGGIE "TO DO'S"

_____

_____

_____

_____

_____

_____

_____

_____

_____

GOAL ACTION STEPS: _____

_____

July Show Calendar: Year _____

2- YEAR PLANNER

SUN	MON	TUES	WED	THU	FRID	SAT

MY UPCOMING SHOWS AND DOGGIE "TO DO'S"

_____

_____

_____

_____

_____

_____

_____

_____

_____

GOAL ACTION STEPS: _____

_____

July Show Calendar: Year _____

SUN	MON	TUES	WED	THU	FRID	SAT

MY UPCOMING SHOWS AND DOGGIE "TO DO'S"

_____

_____

_____

_____

_____

_____

_____

_____

_____

GOAL ACTION STEPS:

_____

August Show Calendar: Year _____

2- YEAR PLANNER

SUN	MON	TUES	WED	THU	FRID	SAT

MY UPCOMING SHOWS AND DOGGIE "TO DO'S"

_____

_____

_____

_____

_____

_____

_____

_____

_____

GOAL ACTION STEPS: _____

_____

August Show Calendar: Year _____

SUN	MON	TUES	WED	THU	FRID	SAT

MY UPCOMING SHOWS AND DOGGIE "TO DO'S"

_____

_____

_____

_____

_____

_____

_____

_____

GOAL ACTION STEPS:

_____

September Show Calendar: Year _____

2- YEAR PLANNER

SUN	MON	TUES	WED	THU	FRID	SAT

MY UPCOMING SHOWS AND DOGGIE "TO DO'S"

_____

_____

_____

_____

_____

_____

_____

_____

_____

_____

GOAL ACTION STEPS:

_____

_____

September Show Calendar: Year _____

SUN	MON	TUES	WED	THU	FRID	SAT

MY UPCOMING SHOWS AND DOGGIE "TO DO'S"

_____

_____

_____

_____

_____

_____

_____

_____

_____

GOAL ACTION STEPS: _____

_____

October Show Calendar: Year _____

2- YEAR PLANNER

SUN	MON	TUES	WED	THU	FRID	SAT

MY UPCOMING SHOWS AND DOGGIE "TO DO'S"

_____

_____

_____

_____

_____

_____

_____

_____

_____

GOAL ACTION STEPS: _____

_____

October Show Calendar: Year _____

SUN	MON	TUES	WED	THU	FRID	SAT

MY UPCOMING SHOWS AND DOGGIE "TO DO'S"

_____

_____

_____

_____

_____

_____

_____

_____

GOAL ACTION STEPS: _____

_____

November Show Calendar: Year _____

2- YEAR PLANNER

SUN	MON	TUES	WED	THU	FRID	SAT

MY UPCOMING SHOWS AND DOGGIE "TO DO'S"

_____

_____

_____

_____

_____

_____

_____

_____

_____

_____

GOAL ACTION STEPS:

_____

November Show Calendar: Year _____

SUN	MON	TUES	WED	THU	FRID	SAT

MY UPCOMING SHOWS AND DOGGIE "TO DO'S"

_____

_____

_____

_____

_____

_____

_____

_____

_____

GOAL ACTION STEPS: _____

_____

December Show Calendar: Year _____

2- YEAR PLANNER

SUN	MON	TUES	WED	THU	FRID	SAT

MY UPCOMING SHOWS AND DOGGIE "TO DO'S"

_____
_____
_____
_____
_____
_____
_____
_____
_____
_____

GOAL ACTION STEPS: _____

_____

December Show Calendar: Year _____

SUN	MON	TUES	WED	THU	FRID	SAT

MY UPCOMING SHOWS AND DOGGIE "TO DO'S"

_____

_____

_____

_____

_____

_____

_____

_____

_____

_____

GOAL ACTION STEPS: _____

Show Team Hub

REGISTERED NAME _____Call Name_____

DOB_____AKC# _____Other registry # _____

Sire_____

Dam_____

Breed _____Color/Markings _____Sex____Microchip#_____

Owner(s) _____

Co-Owner(s) _____

Breeder(s) _____

Handler(s)_____

Title(s) Earned_____

Notes_____

REGISTERED NAME _____Call Name_____

DOB_____AKC# _____Other registry # _____

Sire_____

Dam_____

Breed _____Color/Markings _____Sex____Microchip#_____

Owner(s) _____

Co-Owner(s) _____

Breeder(s) _____

Handler(s)_____

Title(s) Earned_____

Notes_____

Show Team Hub

REGISTERED NAME _____ Call Name _____

DOB _____ AKC# _____ Other registry # _____

Sire _____

Dam _____

Breed _____ Color/Markings _____ Sex _____ Microchip# _____

Owner(s) _____

Co-Owner(s) _____

Breeder(s) _____

Handler(s) _____

Title(s) Earned _____

Notes _____

REGISTERED NAME _____ Call Name _____

DOB _____ AKC# _____ Other registry # _____

Sire _____

Dam _____

Breed _____ Color/Markings _____ Sex _____ Microchip# _____

Owner(s) _____

Co-Owner(s) _____

Breeder(s) _____

Handler(s) _____

Title(s) Earned _____

Notes _____

Show Team Hub

REGISTERED NAME _____Call Name_____

DOB_____AKC# _____Other registry # _____

Sire_____

Dam_____

Breed _____Color/Markings _____Sex_____Microchip#_____

Owner(s) _____

Co-Owner(s) _____

Breeder(s) _____

Handler(s)_____

Title(s) Earned_____

Notes_____

REGISTERED NAME _____Call Name_____

DOB_____AKC# _____Other registry # _____

Sire_____

Dam_____

Breed _____Color/Markings _____Sex_____Microchip#_____

Owner(s) _____

Co-Owner(s) _____

Breeder(s) _____

Handler(s)_____

Title(s) Earned_____

Notes_____

Show Team Hub

REGISTERED NAME _____Call Name_____

DOB_____AKC# _____Other registry # _____

Sire_____

Dam_____

Breed _____Color/Markings _____Sex_____Microchip#_____

Owner(s) _____

Co-Owner(s) _____

Breeder(s) _____

Handler(s)_____

Title(s) Earned_____

Notes_____

REGISTERED NAME _____Call Name_____

DOB_____AKC# _____Other registry # _____

Sire_____

Dam_____

Breed _____Color/Markings _____Sex_____Microchip#_____

Owner(s) _____

Co-Owner(s) _____

Breeder(s) _____

Handler(s)_____

Title(s) Earned_____

Notes_____

Show Team Hub

REGISTERED NAME _____Call Name_____

DOB_____AKC#_____Other registry #_____

Sire_____

Dam_____

Breed _____Color/Markings _____Sex____Microchip#_____

Owner(s) _____

Co-Owner(s) _____

Breeder(s) _____

Handler(s)_____

Title(s) Earned_____

Notes_____

REGISTERED NAME _____Call Name_____

DOB_____AKC#_____Other registry #_____

Sire_____

Dam_____

Breed _____Color/Markings _____Sex____Microchip#_____

Owner(s) _____

Co-Owner(s) _____

Breeder(s) _____

Handler(s)_____

Title(s) Earned_____

Notes_____

Show Team Hub

REGISTERED NAME _____Call Name_____

DOB_____AKC# _____Other registry # _____

Sire_____

Dam_____

Breed _____Color/Markings _____Sex_____Microchip#_____

Owner(s) _____

Co-Owner(s) _____

Breeder(s) _____

Handler(s)_____

Title(s) Earned_____

Notes_____

REGISTERED NAME _____Call Name_____

DOB_____AKC# _____Other registry # _____

Sire_____

Dam_____

Breed _____Color/Markings _____Sex_____Microchip#_____

Owner(s) _____

Co-Owner(s) _____

Breeder(s) _____

Handler(s)_____

Title(s) Earned_____

Notes_____

Dog Show Checklist

Print out this page to reuse before each show. More on show gear and shopping, page 182.

DOG SUPPLIES

- ☐ I.D.tag, collar, harness, regular leash
- ☐ Show lead(s)
- ☐ Tack box with grooming supplies
- ☐ Feeding: water/food bowl, dog food, water jug
- ☐ Favorite treats, bait, toy (bait bag)
- ☐ Canine First Aid Kit/any doggie meds

DOG AREA SUPPLIES

- ☐ Crates, crate pads, comfy blanket
- ☐ Crate fan
- ☐ Dog travel bag
- ☐ Grooming table
- ☐ Exercise pen/Ground cover/shade cover
- ☐ Poop bags/pooper scooper
- ☐ Baby wipes/paper towels/rags
- ☐ Wagon/trolley to carry items

PAPERWORK

- ☐ Dog papers (i.e. registration, shot record)
- ☐ Show Entry form/judging schedule
- ☐ Map to show grounds
- ☐ Money/checkbook
- ☐ Emergency contacts/pet sitter

HUMAN SUPPLIES

- ☐ Show clothes (and a spare if one gets dirty)
- ☐ Lint roller
- ☐ Sunscreen/hat
- ☐ Folding chairs
- ☐ Tent/umbrella
- ☐ Human First Aid Kit
- ☐ Safety pins/rubber bands
- ☐ Sewing kit
- ☐ Camera/Video Camera
- ☐ Cell Phone
- ☐ Personal items: hair ties, makeup, etc.
- ☐ Food/snacks/water bottles (ice/cooler)
- ☐ A positive attitude
- ☐ This record book
- ☐ **And your fabulous dogs**

EXTRAS

- ☐ _____
- ☐ _____
- ☐ _____
- ☐ _____
- ☐ _____

Part 2
Dog Show Log

TO FIND AND ENTER A SHOW

MY POINT SCHEDULE

MY DOG SHOW AFFIRMATIONS

DOG SHOW RESULTS & NOTES

SEE SAMPLE SHOW LOG, PAGE 5

Everyone thinks they have the BEST DOG, and none of them are wrong.
—W.R. Purche

Steps To Find and Enter a Show

1. FIND AN AKC EVENT TO ENTER

- Log on to the AKC website at www.akc.org—type in search bar: "Find an Event."

- Or, log on to Infodog, www.infodog.com, the dog fancier's resource about AKC shows.

- Acquire a *Premium List*—the official announcement of a club's event. It can be obtained from the show secretary or superintendent, at www.akc.org—type in search bar: "Conformation Superintendents." The premium list contains the information about the event— judges panel, classes offered and entry fees.

2. CHOOSE A CLASS TO ENTER

If your dog is not a "Champion of Record," enter them in one of the *regular classes:* (Visit AKC.org to read more)

REGULAR CLASSES: Males (dogs) and females (bitches) compete separately

6-9 Month Puppy: at least 6 months and under 9 months of age.

9-12 Month Puppy: at least 9 months and under 12 months of age.

12-18 Month: at least 12 months and under 18 months. Sometimes divided into 12-15 and 15-18 months.

Novice: dogs that have not won 3 first places in Novice, Amateur-Owner-Handler, Bred-by-Exhibitor, American-bred, or Open Classes, or who've not earned one or more points toward their championship.

Amateur-Owner-Handler: dogs handled by registered owner who has not, at any point, been a professional dog handler, AKC approved conformation judge, or employed as assistant to a professional handler.

Bred-by-Exhibitor: dogs handled and owned by its breeder.

American-Bred: dogs who were bred and born in America.

Open Class: any dog may enter; the only regular class Champions are eligible to compete in.

After regular classes, all first place dogs in a class return to compete to be named Winners Dog (males) or Winners Bitch (females) and earn championship points—these advance to **Best of Breed** judging.

NON-REGULAR CLASSES: Held after regular classes

- Some shows offer non-regular classes. Check your premium list to see if any are available. Non-regular class winners are not eligible to compete for championship points.

- *Veterans Class* is most common non-regular class—for dogs who meet a minimum age set by the club (often for dogs 7 years or older). Winners of the class are eligible to compete for Best of Breed.

- *Special Attractions* are sometimes offered at all-breed, group or specialty shows. These can include:

- **Best Puppy Competition** gives the Puppy Class dog and bitch winners in each breed/variety a chance to be named Best Puppy in Show (BPIS). (If you win your puppy class, stay close!) All the Puppy Class 1st place winners reenter the ring following Best of Breed/Variety judging to determine Best Puppy for that breed/variety. All Best Puppy Breed/Variety winners move on to Puppy Group Competition. The 1st place winners of each of the 7 Puppy Groups then compete for Best Puppy in Show.

- **National Owner-Handled Series** recognizes and celebrates owner-handler exhibitors. Owner-Handlers compete in the regular classes with the NOHS Best of Breed award given following regular judging. *To enter the NOHS, check the owner-handler box on your entry form. It requires no additional fee.*

- **Sweepstakes** are a non-regular competition offered in addition to regular classes. These recognize outstanding puppies and young dogs (Puppy Sweeps) and older dogs (Veteran Sweeps). A separate judge is assigned. Note these judges also in your dog show log. Sweeps are primarily held at specialty shows. Check your premium list to see if sweeps are offered. No championship points are awarded.

3. SUBMIT YOUR SHOW ENTRY

- **Once you've chosen your class, submit your entry** by mailing the printed form or online on the show superintendent's website (see below) or through infodog.com.

  BayRay Event Services, Inc.: www.barayevents.com (360) 755-7086

  Foy Trent Dog Shows: www.foytrentdogshows.com (573) 687-2101

  Jack Bradshaw Dog Shows: www.jbradshaw.com (323) 727-0136

  Jack Onofrio Dog Shows, L.L.C.: www.onofrio.com (405) 427-8181

  MB-F, Inc.: Email: www.infodog.com Phone: (336) 379-9352

  Rau Dog Shows, Ltd.: www.raudogshows.com/ (610) 376-1880

Helpful links, visit akc.org. type in search bar

- How to Complete a Show Entry (one entry per dog)

- How to Select a Class

- AKC Event Cancelations

- Conformation: Frequently Asked Questions

Training opportunites, visit akc.org. type in search bar

- 4-6 Month Beginner Puppy Competition

- AKC Match Program (Events often used as practice for puppies and their owners)

Some alternatives to "AKC" dog shows

- UKC Shows: The United Kennel Club shows (UKC), www.ukcdogs.com/

- IABCA Shows: The International All Breed Canine Association Shows, www.iabca.com/

- CKC shows: The Canadian Kennel Club, www.ckc.ca/en/Events

TIPS TO KEEP IN MIND WHEN ENTERING A SHOW

- Use your "Dog Show Hub" (pg. 34-39) to keep your dogs registration certificate information. You will need this to easily fill out your show entries.

- Be sure to enter your event by the date and time listed on the premium list. A confirmation of your entry with the *judging schedule* (this tells you the time your dog will show and ring number) should arrive to you about one week before the show. If you have not received your entry, contact the show superintendent or show chairman listed in your premium list.

- Confirm entry details (class entred, etc.) and promptly contact the show superintendent to rectify any errors.

About the AKC Point Schedule

In the AKC show catalog, you will see a point schedule for your breed that looks similar to this:

POINTS	D ^{1} B		D ^{2} B		D ^{3} B		D ^{4} B		D ^{5} B	
ALL OTHER BREEDS & VARIETIES	2	2	3	3	4	4	5	5	6	6

TO FIGURE YOUR POINTS

- Count dogs competing in the regular classes of your dog's sex. Then compare that number to the point schedule in your catalog. Look at these two examples and refer above to the chart.

   WINNERS DOG — WD (3 dogs = 2 pts)   **WINNERS BITCH — WB (4 bitches = 3 pts)**

- When counting dogs in competition, only count dogs present that are judged.

- **For more information, visit www.akc.org. Type in the search bar:**

   Point Schedule

   How to Count Points at AKC Dog Shows

   How to Count Grand Champion points

TO FILL IN YOUR POINT SCHEDULE **ON THE NEXT PAGE**

1. Visit www.akc.org. Type in the search bar, "Point Schedule." A list of *Divisions* will appear.

2. Scroll down to find your division—the state where your dog is showing.

3. Scroll to find the breed of dog you show. Note how many dogs and bitches it takes to earn 1-5 points.

4. Then fill out the charts on the following page.

5. Use the charts for quick reference while at shows to confirm how many points your dog earned.

6. Check the AKC website occasionally, as point schedules can change.

There are 15 divisions, and point schedules vary by location. Seven charts are provided on the next page in case you travel to various regions and change divisions, or if you show more than one breed. Ensure you obtain the point schedule for the region where your dog won.

POINTS, AWARD, RIBBONS, AND TITLES EXPLAINED

- Page 170: How to Count Championship Points

- Page 172: AKC Award and Ribbons

- Page 174: AKC Titles and Meanings

Refer to the point schedule while at shows to confirm points earned.

Point schedule for division:

POINTS	D ^{1} B	D ^{2} B	D ^{3} B	D ^{4} B	D ^{5} B
YOUR BREED					

Point schedule for division:

POINTS	D ^{1} B	D ^{2} B	D ^{3} B	D ^{4} B	D ^{5} B
YOUR BREED					

Point schedule for division:

POINTS	D ^{1} B	D ^{2} B	D ^{3} B	D ^{4} B	D ^{5} B
YOUR BREED					

Point schedule for division:

POINTS	D ^{1} B	D ^{2} B	D ^{3} B	D ^{4} B	D ^{5} B
YOUR BREED					

Point schedule for division:

POINTS	D ^{1} B	D ^{2} B	D ^{3} B	D ^{4} B	D ^{5} B
YOUR BREED					

Point schedule for division:

POINTS	D ^{1} B	D ^{2} B	D ^{3} B	D ^{4} B	D ^{5} B
YOUR BREED					

Point schedule for division:

POINTS	D ^{1} B	D ^{2} B	D ^{3} B	D ^{4} B	D ^{5} B
YOUR BREED					

Be sure you obtain the point schedule for the region where your dog won.

My Dog Show Affirmations

POSITIVE AFFIRMATIONS ARE A POWERFUL WAY for you, as a dog show competitor, to create a winning mindset. By doing affirmations regularly, you can improve your self-image and overcome ways of thinking that may be holding you back from being your best. Below are 10 sample affirmations. At the bottom of each competition log is a space to write your "dog show positive affirmation." Write it at least a week before the show and say it regularly to build confidence. *More about nurturing a winning mindset p.162.*

Tips for writing your own: (1) Write your affirmation in the present tense. (2) Don't use negative statements, i.e., I won't lose today. Instead, focus on the positive, i.e., I am a winner! (3) Write what you "want" to come true even though it may not be a reality yet. (4) Keep your affirmations short and easy to recall.

10 AFFIRMATIONS FOR DOG SHOW COMPETITORS:

1. I constantly learn, grow, and work hard to improve my handling skills.

2. I help my dog to show his best and win.

3. I am mentally strong and perform well under pressure.

4. I am a good sportsman and kind to all.

5. I set goals and take steps to see them through.

6. I take care of my body and mind.

7. My dog is shiny, well-trained, and show-ready!

8. My dog and I share a beautiful bond.

9. I present my dog to the judge with excellence and professionalism.

10. I am a winner! My dog is a winner!

Practice writing your own dog show affirmations on the next page.

Remember: Your affirmations are unique to your goals. Don't compare them to others. Also, don't let others get you down by saying your aspirations are "unrealistic." Dreaming big requires us to rise to a challenge and reach for the stars to realize our dreams. Will your dreams come true right away? Maybe, maybe not. Either way, you are doing your best to move from dreams to reality by staying positive.

**DREAMING BIG REQUIRES US TO RISE TO A CHALLENGE AND REACH
FOR THE STARS IN ORDER TO REALIZE OUR DREAMS!**

My Positive Dog Show Affirmations

1. _____
2. _____
3. _____
4. _____
5. _____
6. _____
7. _____
8. _____
9. _____
10. _____
11. _____
12. _____
13. _____
14. _____
15. _____
16. _____
17. _____
18. _____
19. _____
20. _____

Bring this book with you to your dog shows and refer to this page for extra motivation.

Dog Show Competition Log

SHOW DATE	NAME OF DOG/ARM BAND NUMBER	EVENT TYPE	NAME OF SHOW

CLASS ENTERED	PLACE IN CLASS	ENTRY IN CLASS	TOTAL ENTRY	POINTS	AWARD	GROUP	BEST IN SHOW

ENTRY BREAK DOWN_____RING #_____TIME_____BREEDS BEFORE_____

BREED JUDGE _____GROUP _____BIS _____

AWARDS TODAY_____

POINTS COMING IN SHOW _____ POINTS EARNED TODAY _____ POINTS TO DATE _____

OTHER RESULTS/JUDGES (I.E. NOHS)_____

_____

NEW TITLE _____

COMMENTS AND TAKE-AWAYS

_____

_____

_____

_____

_____

SHOW PREPARATIONS AND FEES

SHOW ADDRESS/ETA _____

SHOW PHOTO TAKEN [YES] [NO] PHOTO SENT TO JUDGE [YES] [NO] PHOTOGRAPHER _____

FEES: ENTRY_____ PHOTOS_____ PARKING_____ GROOMING_____ HEALTH CLINICS_____

HANDLER NAME/FEE _____HEALTH CLINIC TIMES_____

HOTEL _____PET SITTER_____

THINGS TO REMEMBER _____

TODAY'S GOAL _____

POSITIVE AFFIRMATION _____

Dog Show Competition Log

SHOW DATE	NAME OF DOG/ARM BAND NUMBER	EVENT TYPE	NAME OF SHOW

CLASS ENTERED	PLACE IN CLASS	ENTRY IN CLASS	TOTAL ENTRY	POINTS	AWARD	GROUP	BEST IN SHOW

ENTRY BREAK DOWN_____RING #_____TIME_____BREEDS BEFORE_____

BREED JUDGE _____GROUP _____BIS _____

AWARDS TODAY_____

POINTS COMING IN SHOW _____ POINTS EARNED TODAY _____ POINTS TO DATE _____

OTHER RESULTS/JUDGES (I.E. NOHS)_____

_____

NEW TITLE _____

COMMENTS AND TAKE-AWAYS

_____

_____

_____

_____

_____

SHOW PREPARATIONS AND FEES

SHOW ADDRESS/ETA _____

SHOW PHOTO TAKEN [YES] [NO] PHOTO SENT TO JUDGE [YES] [NO] PHOTOGRAPHER_____

FEES: ENTRY_____ PHOTOS_____ PARKING_____ GROOMING_____ HEALTH CLINICS_____

HANDLER NAME/FEE _____HEALTH CLINIC TIMES_____

HOTEL _____PET SITTER_____

THINGS TO REMEMBER _____

TODAY'S GOAL _____

POSITIVE AFFIRMATION _____

Dog Show Competition Log

SHOW DATE	NAME OF DOG/ARM BAND NUMBER	EVENT TYPE	NAME OF SHOW

CLASS ENTERED	PLACE IN CLASS	ENTRY IN CLASS	TOTAL ENTRY	POINTS	AWARD	GROUP	BEST IN SHOW

ENTRY BREAK DOWN_____RING #_____TIME_____BREEDS BEFORE_____

BREED JUDGE _____GROUP _____ BIS _____

AWARDS TODAY_____

POINTS COMING IN SHOW _____ POINTS EARNED TODAY _____ POINTS TO DATE _____

OTHER RESULTS/JUDGES (I.E. NOHS)_____

_____

NEW TITLE _____

COMMENTS AND TAKE-AWAYS

_____

_____

_____

_____

_____

SHOW PREPARATIONS AND FEES

SHOW ADDRESS/ETA _____

SHOW PHOTO TAKEN [YES] [NO] PHOTO SENT TO JUDGE [YES] [NO] PHOTOGRAPHER_____

FEES: ENTRY_____ PHOTOS_____ PARKING_____ GROOMING_____ HEALTH CLINICS_____

HANDLER NAME/FEE _____HEALTH CLINIC TIMES_____

HOTEL _____PET SITTER_____

THINGS TO REMEMBER _____

TODAY'S GOAL _____

POSITIVE AFFIRMATION _____

Dog Show Competition Log

SHOW DATE	NAME OF DOG/ARM BAND NUMBER	EVENT TYPE	NAME OF SHOW

CLASS ENTERED	PLACE IN CLASS	ENTRY IN CLASS	TOTAL ENTRY	POINTS	AWARD	GROUP	BEST IN SHOW

ENTRY BREAK DOWN_____RING #_____TIME_____BREEDS BEFORE_____

BREED JUDGE _____GROUP _____BIS _____

AWARDS TODAY_____

POINTS COMING IN SHOW _____ POINTS EARNED TODAY _____ POINTS TO DATE _____

OTHER RESULTS/JUDGES (I.E. NOHS)_____

_____

NEW TITLE _____

COMMENTS AND TAKE-AWAYS

_____
_____
_____
_____
_____

SHOW PREPARATIONS AND FEES

SHOW ADDRESS/ETA _____

SHOW PHOTO TAKEN [YES] [NO] PHOTO SENT TO JUDGE [YES] [NO] PHOTOGRAPHER _____

FEES: ENTRY_____ PHOTOS_____ PARKING_____ GROOMING_____ HEALTH CLINICS_____

HANDLER NAME/FEE _____HEALTH CLINIC TIMES_____

HOTEL _____PET SITTER_____

THINGS TO REMEMBER _____

TODAY'S GOAL _____

POSITIVE AFFIRMATION _____

Dog Show Competition Log

SHOW DATE	NAME OF DOG/ARM BAND NUMBER	EVENT TYPE	NAME OF SHOW

CLASS ENTERED	PLACE IN CLASS	ENTRY IN CLASS	TOTAL ENTRY	POINTS	AWARD	GROUP	BEST IN SHOW

ENTRY BREAK DOWN_____RING #_____TIME_____BREEDS BEFORE_____

BREED JUDGE _____GROUP _____BIS _____

AWARDS TODAY_____

POINTS COMING IN SHOW _____ POINTS EARNED TODAY _____ POINTS TO DATE _____

OTHER RESULTS/JUDGES (I.E. NOHS)_____

_____

NEW TITLE _____

COMMENTS AND TAKE-AWAYS

_____

_____

_____

_____

_____

SHOW PREPARATIONS AND FEES

SHOW ADDRESS/ETA _____

SHOW PHOTO TAKEN ☐ YES ☐ NO   PHOTO SENT TO JUDGE ☐ YES ☐ NO   PHOTOGRAPHER _____

FEES: ENTRY_____ PHOTOS_____ PARKING_____ GROOMING_____ HEALTH CLINICS_____

HANDLER NAME/FEE _____HEALTH CLINIC TIMES_____

HOTEL _____PET SITTER_____

THINGS TO REMEMBER _____

TODAY'S GOAL _____

POSITIVE AFFIRMATION _____

Dog Show Competition Log

SHOW DATE	NAME OF DOG/ARM BAND NUMBER	EVENT TYPE	NAME OF SHOW

CLASS ENTERED	PLACE IN CLASS	ENTRY IN CLASS	TOTAL ENTRY	POINTS	AWARD	GROUP	BEST IN SHOW

ENTRY BREAK DOWN_____RING #_____TIME_____BREEDS BEFORE_____

BREED JUDGE _____GROUP _____BIS _____

AWARDS TODAY_____

POINTS COMING IN SHOW _____ POINTS EARNED TODAY _____ POINTS TO DATE _____

OTHER RESULTS/JUDGES (I.E. NOHS)_____

_____

NEW TITLE _____

COMMENTS AND TAKE-AWAYS

_____

_____

_____

_____

_____

SHOW PREPARATIONS AND FEES

SHOW ADDRESS/ETA _____

SHOW PHOTO TAKEN ☐ YES ☐ NO PHOTO SENT TO JUDGE ☐ YES ☐ NO PHOTOGRAPHER _____

FEES: ENTRY_____ PHOTOS_____ PARKING_____ GROOMING_____ HEALTH CLINICS_____

HANDLER NAME/FEE _____HEALTH CLINIC TIMES_____

HOTEL _____PET SITTER_____

THINGS TO REMEMBER _____

TODAY'S GOAL _____

POSITIVE AFFIRMATION _____

Dog Show Competition Log

SHOW DATE	NAME OF DOG/ARM BAND NUMBER	EVENT TYPE	NAME OF SHOW

CLASS ENTERED	PLACE IN CLASS	ENTRY IN CLASS	TOTAL ENTRY	POINTS	AWARD	GROUP	BEST IN SHOW

ENTRY BREAK DOWN_____RING #_____TIME_____BREEDS BEFORE_____

BREED JUDGE _____GROUP _____ BIS _____

AWARDS TODAY_____

POINTS COMING IN SHOW _____ POINTS EARNED TODAY _____ POINTS TO DATE _____

OTHER RESULTS/JUDGES (I.E. NOHS)_____

_____

NEW TITLE _____

COMMENTS AND TAKE-AWAYS

_____

_____

_____

_____

_____

SHOW PREPARATIONS AND FEES

SHOW ADDRESS/ETA _____

SHOW PHOTO TAKEN [YES] [NO] PHOTO SENT TO JUDGE [YES] [NO] PHOTOGRAPHER_____

FEES: ENTRY_____ PHOTOS_____ PARKING_____ GROOMING_____ HEALTH CLINICS_____

HANDLER NAME/FEE _____HEALTH CLINIC TIMES_____

HOTEL _____PET SITTER_____

THINGS TO REMEMBER _____

TODAY'S GOAL _____

POSITIVE AFFIRMATION _____

Dog Show Competition Log

SHOW DATE	NAME OF DOG/ARM BAND NUMBER	EVENT TYPE	NAME OF SHOW

CLASS ENTERED	PLACE IN CLASS	ENTRY IN CLASS	TOTAL ENTRY	POINTS	AWARD	GROUP	BEST IN SHOW

ENTRY BREAK DOWN_____RING #_____TIME_____BREEDS BEFORE_____

BREED JUDGE _____GROUP _____BIS _____

AWARDS TODAY_____

POINTS COMING IN SHOW _____ POINTS EARNED TODAY _____ POINTS TO DATE _____

OTHER RESULTS/JUDGES (I.E. NOHS)_____

_____

NEW TITLE _____

COMMENTS AND TAKE-AWAYS

_____

_____

_____

_____

_____

SHOW PREPARATIONS AND FEES

SHOW ADDRESS/ETA _____

SHOW PHOTO TAKEN [YES] [NO] PHOTO SENT TO JUDGE [YES] [NO] PHOTOGRAPHER _____

FEES: ENTRY_____ PHOTOS_____ PARKING_____ GROOMING_____ HEALTH CLINICS_____

HANDLER NAME/FEE _____HEALTH CLINIC TIMES_____

HOTEL _____PET SITTER_____

THINGS TO REMEMBER _____

TODAY'S GOAL _____

POSITIVE AFFIRMATION _____

Dog Show Competition Log

SHOW DATE	NAME OF DOG/ARM BAND NUMBER	EVENT TYPE	NAME OF SHOW

CLASS ENTERED	PLACE IN CLASS	ENTRY IN CLASS	TOTAL ENTRY	POINTS	AWARD	GROUP	BEST IN SHOW

ENTRY BREAK DOWN_____RING #_____TIME_____BREEDS BEFORE_____

BREED JUDGE _____GROUP _____BIS _____

AWARDS TODAY_____

POINTS COMING IN SHOW _____ POINTS EARNED TODAY _____ POINTS TO DATE _____

OTHER RESULTS/JUDGES (I.E. NOHS)_____

_____

NEW TITLE _____

COMMENTS AND TAKE-AWAYS

_____

_____

_____

_____

_____

SHOW PREPARATIONS AND FEES

SHOW ADDRESS/ETA _____

SHOW PHOTO TAKEN [YES] [NO] PHOTO SENT TO JUDGE [YES] [NO] PHOTOGRAPHER _____

FEES: ENTRY_____ PHOTOS_____ PARKING_____ GROOMING_____ HEALTH CLINICS_____

HANDLER NAME/FEE _____HEALTH CLINIC TIMES_____

HOTEL _____PET SITTER_____

THINGS TO REMEMBER _____

TODAY'S GOAL _____

POSITIVE AFFIRMATION _____

Dog Show Competition Log

SHOW DATE	NAME OF DOG/ARM BAND NUMBER	EVENT TYPE	NAME OF SHOW

CLASS ENTERED	PLACE IN CLASS	ENTRY IN CLASS	TOTAL ENTRY	POINTS	AWARD	GROUP	BEST IN SHOW

ENTRY BREAK DOWN_____RING #_____TIME_____BREEDS BEFORE_____

BREED JUDGE _____GROUP _____BIS _____

AWARDS TODAY_____

POINTS COMING IN SHOW _____ POINTS EARNED TODAY _____ POINTS TO DATE _____

OTHER RESULTS/JUDGES (I.E. NOHS)_____

_____

NEW TITLE _____

COMMENTS AND TAKE-AWAYS

_____

_____

_____

_____

_____

SHOW PREPARATIONS AND FEES

SHOW ADDRESS/ETA _____

SHOW PHOTO TAKEN [YES] [NO] PHOTO SENT TO JUDGE [YES] [NO] PHOTOGRAPHER_____

FEES: ENTRY_____ PHOTOS_____ PARKING_____ GROOMING_____ HEALTH CLINICS_____

HANDLER NAME/FEE _____HEALTH CLINIC TIMES_____

HOTEL _____PET SITTER_____

THINGS TO REMEMBER _____

TODAY'S GOAL _____

POSITIVE AFFIRMATION _____

Dog Show Competition Log

SHOW DATE	NAME OF DOG/ARM BAND NUMBER	EVENT TYPE	NAME OF SHOW

CLASS ENTERED	PLACE IN CLASS	ENTRY IN CLASS	TOTAL ENTRY	POINTS	AWARD	GROUP	BEST IN SHOW

ENTRY BREAK DOWN_____RING #_____TIME_____BREEDS BEFORE_____

BREED JUDGE _____GROUP _____ BIS _____

AWARDS TODAY_____

POINTS COMING IN SHOW _____ POINTS EARNED TODAY _____ POINTS TO DATE _____

OTHER RESULTS/JUDGES (I.E. NOHS)_____

_____

NEW TITLE _____

COMMENTS AND TAKE-AWAYS

_____

_____

_____

_____

_____

SHOW PREPARATIONS AND FEES

SHOW ADDRESS/ETA _____

SHOW PHOTO TAKEN [YES] [NO] PHOTO SENT TO JUDGE [YES] [NO] PHOTOGRAPHER_____

FEES: ENTRY_____ PHOTOS_____ PARKING_____ GROOMING_____ HEALTH CLINICS_____

HANDLER NAME/FEE _____HEALTH CLINIC TIMES_____

HOTEL _____PET SITTER_____

THINGS TO REMEMBER _____

TODAY'S GOAL _____

POSITIVE AFFIRMATION _____

Dog Show Competition Log

SHOW DATE	NAME OF DOG/ARM BAND NUMBER	EVENT TYPE	NAME OF SHOW

CLASS ENTERED	PLACE IN CLASS	ENTRY IN CLASS	TOTAL ENTRY	POINTS	AWARD	GROUP	BEST IN SHOW

ENTRY BREAK DOWN_____RING #_____TIME_____BREEDS BEFORE_____

BREED JUDGE _____GROUP _____ BIS _____

AWARDS TODAY_____

POINTS COMING IN SHOW _____ POINTS EARNED TODAY _____ POINTS TO DATE _____

OTHER RESULTS/JUDGES (I.E. NOHS)_____

_____

NEW TITLE _____

COMMENTS AND TAKE-AWAYS

_____

_____

_____

_____

_____

SHOW PREPARATIONS AND FEES

SHOW ADDRESS/ETA _____

SHOW PHOTO TAKEN [YES] [NO] PHOTO SENT TO JUDGE [YES] [NO] PHOTOGRAPHER _____

FEES: ENTRY_____ PHOTOS_____ PARKING_____ GROOMING_____ HEALTH CLINICS_____

HANDLER NAME/FEE _____HEALTH CLINIC TIMES_____

HOTEL _____PET SITTER_____

THINGS TO REMEMBER _____

TODAY'S GOAL _____

POSITIVE AFFIRMATION _____

Dog Show Competition Log

SHOW DATE	NAME OF DOG/ARM BAND NUMBER	EVENT TYPE	NAME OF SHOW

CLASS ENTERED	PLACE IN CLASS	ENTRY IN CLASS	TOTAL ENTRY	POINTS	AWARD	GROUP	BEST IN SHOW

ENTRY BREAK DOWN_____RING #_____TIME_____BREEDS BEFORE_____

BREED JUDGE _____GROUP _____ BIS _____

AWARDS TODAY_____

POINTS COMING IN SHOW _____ POINTS EARNED TODAY _____ POINTS TO DATE _____

OTHER RESULTS/JUDGES (I.E. NOHS)_____

_____

NEW TITLE _____

COMMENTS AND TAKE-AWAYS

_____

_____

_____

_____

_____

SHOW PREPARATIONS AND FEES

SHOW ADDRESS/ETA _____

SHOW PHOTO TAKEN [YES] [NO] PHOTO SENT TO JUDGE [YES] [NO] PHOTOGRAPHER _____

FEES: ENTRY_____ PHOTOS_____ PARKING_____ GROOMING_____ HEALTH CLINICS_____

HANDLER NAME/FEE _____HEALTH CLINIC TIMES_____

HOTEL _____PET SITTER_____

THINGS TO REMEMBER _____

TODAY'S GOAL _____

POSITIVE AFFIRMATION _____

Dog Show Competition Log

SHOW DATE	NAME OF DOG/ARM BAND NUMBER	EVENT TYPE	NAME OF SHOW

CLASS ENTERED	PLACE IN CLASS	ENTRY IN CLASS	TOTAL ENTRY	POINTS	AWARD	GROUP	BEST IN SHOW

ENTRY BREAK DOWN_____RING #_____TIME_____BREEDS BEFORE_____

BREED JUDGE _____GROUP _____BIS _____

AWARDS TODAY_____

POINTS COMING IN SHOW _____ POINTS EARNED TODAY _____ POINTS TO DATE _____

OTHER RESULTS/JUDGES (I.E. NOHS)_____

_____

NEW TITLE _____

COMMENTS AND TAKE-AWAYS

_____

_____

_____

_____

_____

SHOW PREPARATIONS AND FEES

SHOW ADDRESS/ETA _____

SHOW PHOTO TAKEN [YES] [NO] PHOTO SENT TO JUDGE [YES] [NO] PHOTOGRAPHER _____

FEES: ENTRY_____ PHOTOS_____ PARKING_____ GROOMING_____ HEALTH CLINICS_____

HANDLER NAME/FEE _____HEALTH CLINIC TIMES_____

HOTEL _____PET SITTER_____

THINGS TO REMEMBER _____

TODAY'S GOAL _____

POSITIVE AFFIRMATION _____

Dog Show Competition Log

SHOW DATE	NAME OF DOG/ARM BAND NUMBER	EVENT TYPE	NAME OF SHOW

CLASS ENTERED	PLACE IN CLASS	ENTRY IN CLASS	TOTAL ENTRY	POINTS	AWARD	GROUP	BEST IN SHOW

ENTRY BREAK DOWN_____RING #_____TIME_____BREEDS BEFORE_____

BREED JUDGE _____GROUP _____ BIS _____

AWARDS TODAY_____

POINTS COMING IN SHOW _____ POINTS EARNED TODAY _____ POINTS TO DATE _____

OTHER RESULTS/JUDGES (I.E. NOHS)_____

_____

NEW TITLE _____

COMMENTS AND TAKE-AWAYS

_____

_____

_____

_____

_____

SHOW PREPARATIONS AND FEES

SHOW ADDRESS/ETA _____

SHOW PHOTO TAKEN [YES] [NO] PHOTO SENT TO JUDGE [YES] [NO] PHOTOGRAPHER_____

FEES: ENTRY_____ PHOTOS_____ PARKING_____ GROOMING_____ HEALTH CLINICS_____

HANDLER NAME/FEE _____HEALTH CLINIC TIMES_____

HOTEL _____PET SITTER_____

THINGS TO REMEMBER _____

TODAY'S GOAL _____

POSITIVE AFFIRMATION _____

Dog Show Competition Log

SHOW DATE	NAME OF DOG/ARM BAND NUMBER	EVENT TYPE	NAME OF SHOW

CLASS ENTERED	PLACE IN CLASS	ENTRY IN CLASS	TOTAL ENTRY	POINTS	AWARD	GROUP	BEST IN SHOW

ENTRY BREAK DOWN_____RING #_____TIME_____BREEDS BEFORE_____

BREED JUDGE _____GROUP _____ BIS _____

AWARDS TODAY_____

POINTS COMING IN SHOW _____ POINTS EARNED TODAY _____ POINTS TO DATE _____

OTHER RESULTS/JUDGES (I.E. NOHS)_____

_____

NEW TITLE _____

COMMENTS AND TAKE-AWAYS

_____

_____

_____

_____

_____

SHOW PREPARATIONS AND FEES

SHOW ADDRESS/ETA _____

SHOW PHOTO TAKEN [YES] [NO] PHOTO SENT TO JUDGE [YES] [NO] PHOTOGRAPHER _____

FEES: ENTRY_____ PHOTOS_____ PARKING_____ GROOMING_____ HEALTH CLINICS_____

HANDLER NAME/FEE _____HEALTH CLINIC TIMES_____

HOTEL _____PET SITTER_____

THINGS TO REMEMBER _____

TODAY'S GOAL _____

POSITIVE AFFIRMATION _____

Dog Show Competition Log

SHOW DATE	NAME OF DOG/ARM BAND NUMBER	EVENT TYPE	NAME OF SHOW

CLASS ENTERED	PLACE IN CLASS	ENTRY IN CLASS	TOTAL ENTRY	POINTS	AWARD	GROUP	BEST IN SHOW

ENTRY BREAK DOWN_____RING #_____TIME_____BREEDS BEFORE_____

BREED JUDGE _____GROUP _____BIS _____

AWARDS TODAY_____

POINTS COMING IN SHOW _____ POINTS EARNED TODAY _____ POINTS TO DATE _____

OTHER RESULTS/JUDGES (I.E. NOHS)_____

_____

NEW TITLE _____

COMMENTS AND TAKE-AWAYS

_____

_____

_____

_____

_____

SHOW PREPARATIONS AND FEES

SHOW ADDRESS/ETA _____

SHOW PHOTO TAKEN [YES] [NO] PHOTO SENT TO JUDGE [YES] [NO] PHOTOGRAPHER _____

FEES: ENTRY_____ PHOTOS_____ PARKING_____ GROOMING_____ HEALTH CLINICS_____

HANDLER NAME/FEE _____HEALTH CLINIC TIMES_____

HOTEL _____PET SITTER_____

THINGS TO REMEMBER _____

TODAY'S GOAL _____

POSITIVE AFFIRMATION _____

Dog Show Competition Log

SHOW DATE	NAME OF DOG/ARM BAND NUMBER	EVENT TYPE	NAME OF SHOW

CLASS ENTERED	PLACE IN CLASS	ENTRY IN CLASS	TOTAL ENTRY	POINTS	AWARD	GROUP	BEST IN SHOW

ENTRY BREAK DOWN_____RING #_____TIME_____BREEDS BEFORE_____

BREED JUDGE _____GROUP _____BIS _____

AWARDS TODAY_____

POINTS COMING IN SHOW _____ POINTS EARNED TODAY _____ POINTS TO DATE _____

OTHER RESULTS/JUDGES (I.E. NOHS)_____

_____

NEW TITLE _____

COMMENTS AND TAKE-AWAYS

_____

_____

_____

_____

_____

SHOW PREPARATIONS AND FEES

SHOW ADDRESS/ETA _____

SHOW PHOTO TAKEN [YES] [NO] PHOTO SENT TO JUDGE [YES] [NO] PHOTOGRAPHER _____

FEES: ENTRY_____ PHOTOS_____ PARKING_____ GROOMING_____ HEALTH CLINICS_____

HANDLER NAME/FEE _____HEALTH CLINIC TIMES_____

HOTEL _____PET SITTER_____

THINGS TO REMEMBER _____

TODAY'S GOAL _____

POSITIVE AFFIRMATION _____

Dog Show Competition Log

SHOW DATE	NAME OF DOG/ARM BAND NUMBER	EVENT TYPE	NAME OF SHOW

CLASS ENTERED	PLACE IN CLASS	ENTRY IN CLASS	TOTAL ENTRY	POINTS	AWARD	GROUP	BEST IN SHOW

ENTRY BREAK DOWN_____RING #_____TIME_____BREEDS BEFORE_____

BREED JUDGE _____GROUP _____ BIS _____

AWARDS TODAY_____

POINTS COMING IN SHOW _____ POINTS EARNED TODAY _____ POINTS TO DATE _____

OTHER RESULTS/JUDGES (I.E. NOHS)_____

_____

NEW TITLE _____

COMMENTS AND TAKE-AWAYS

_____

_____

_____

_____

_____

SHOW PREPARATIONS AND FEES

SHOW ADDRESS/ETA _____

SHOW PHOTO TAKEN ☐ YES ☐ NO   PHOTO SENT TO JUDGE ☐ YES ☐ NO   PHOTOGRAPHER_____

FEES: ENTRY_____ PHOTOS_____ PARKING_____ GROOMING_____ HEALTH CLINICS_____

HANDLER NAME/FEE _____HEALTH CLINIC TIMES_____

HOTEL _____PET SITTER_____

THINGS TO REMEMBER _____

TODAY'S GOAL _____

POSITIVE AFFIRMATION _____

Dog Show Competition Log

SHOW DATE	NAME OF DOG/ARM BAND NUMBER	EVENT TYPE	NAME OF SHOW

CLASS ENTERED	PLACE IN CLASS	ENTRY IN CLASS	TOTAL ENTRY	POINTS	AWARD	GROUP	BEST IN SHOW

ENTRY BREAK DOWN_____RING #_____TIME_____BREEDS BEFORE_____

BREED JUDGE _____GROUP _____ BIS _____

AWARDS TODAY_____

POINTS COMING IN SHOW _____ POINTS EARNED TODAY _____ POINTS TO DATE _____

OTHER RESULTS/JUDGES (I.E. NOHS)_____

_____

NEW TITLE _____

COMMENTS AND TAKE-AWAYS

_____

_____

_____

_____

_____

SHOW PREPARATIONS AND FEES

SHOW ADDRESS/ETA _____

SHOW PHOTO TAKEN [YES] [NO] PHOTO SENT TO JUDGE [YES] [NO] PHOTOGRAPHER _____

FEES: ENTRY_____ PHOTOS_____ PARKING_____ GROOMING_____ HEALTH CLINICS_____

HANDLER NAME/FEE _____HEALTH CLINIC TIMES_____

HOTEL _____PET SITTER_____

THINGS TO REMEMBER _____

TODAY'S GOAL _____

POSITIVE AFFIRMATION _____

Dog Show Competition Log

SHOW DATE	NAME OF DOG/ARM BAND NUMBER	EVENT TYPE	NAME OF SHOW

CLASS ENTERED	PLACE IN CLASS	ENTRY IN CLASS	TOTAL ENTRY	POINTS	AWARD	GROUP	BEST IN SHOW

ENTRY BREAK DOWN_____RING #_____TIME_____BREEDS BEFORE_____

BREED JUDGE _____GROUP _____BIS _____

AWARDS TODAY_____

POINTS COMING IN SHOW _____ POINTS EARNED TODAY _____ POINTS TO DATE _____

OTHER RESULTS/JUDGES (I.E. NOHS)_____

_____

NEW TITLE _____

COMMENTS AND TAKE-AWAYS

_____

_____

_____

_____

_____

SHOW PREPARATIONS AND FEES

SHOW ADDRESS/ETA _____

SHOW PHOTO TAKEN [YES] [NO] PHOTO SENT TO JUDGE [YES] [NO] PHOTOGRAPHER _____

FEES: ENTRY_____ PHOTOS_____ PARKING_____ GROOMING_____ HEALTH CLINICS_____

HANDLER NAME/FEE _____HEALTH CLINIC TIMES_____

HOTEL _____PET SITTER_____

THINGS TO REMEMBER _____

TODAY'S GOAL _____

POSITIVE AFFIRMATION _____

Dog Show Competition Log

SHOW DATE	NAME OF DOG/ARM BAND NUMBER	EVENT TYPE	NAME OF SHOW

CLASS ENTERED	PLACE IN CLASS	ENTRY IN CLASS	TOTAL ENTRY	POINTS	AWARD	GROUP	BEST IN SHOW

ENTRY BREAK DOWN_____RING #_____TIME_____BREEDS BEFORE_____

BREED JUDGE _____GROUP _____BIS _____

AWARDS TODAY_____

POINTS COMING IN SHOW _____ POINTS EARNED TODAY _____ POINTS TO DATE _____

OTHER RESULTS/JUDGES (I.E. NOHS)_____

_____

NEW TITLE _____

COMMENTS AND TAKE-AWAYS

_____

_____

_____

_____

_____

SHOW PREPARATIONS AND FEES

SHOW ADDRESS/ETA _____

SHOW PHOTO TAKEN [YES] [NO] PHOTO SENT TO JUDGE [YES] [NO] PHOTOGRAPHER _____

FEES: ENTRY_____ PHOTOS_____ PARKING_____ GROOMING_____ HEALTH CLINICS_____

HANDLER NAME/FEE _____HEALTH CLINIC TIMES_____

HOTEL _____PET SITTER_____

THINGS TO REMEMBER _____

TODAY'S GOAL _____

POSITIVE AFFIRMATION _____

Dog Show Competition Log

SHOW DATE	NAME OF DOG/ARM BAND NUMBER	EVENT TYPE	NAME OF SHOW

CLASS ENTERED	PLACE IN CLASS	ENTRY IN CLASS	TOTAL ENTRY	POINTS	AWARD	GROUP	BEST IN SHOW

ENTRY BREAK DOWN_____RING #_____TIME_____BREEDS BEFORE_____

BREED JUDGE _____GROUP _____ BIS _____

AWARDS TODAY_____

POINTS COMING IN SHOW _____ POINTS EARNED TODAY _____ POINTS TO DATE _____

OTHER RESULTS/JUDGES (I.E. NOHS)_____

_____

NEW TITLE _____

COMMENTS AND TAKE-AWAYS

_____

_____

_____

_____

_____

SHOW PREPARATIONS AND FEES

SHOW ADDRESS/ETA _____

SHOW PHOTO TAKEN [YES] [NO] PHOTO SENT TO JUDGE [YES] [NO] PHOTOGRAPHER_____

FEES: ENTRY_____ PHOTOS_____ PARKING_____ GROOMING_____ HEALTH CLINICS_____

HANDLER NAME/FEE _____HEALTH CLINIC TIMES_____

HOTEL _____PET SITTER_____

THINGS TO REMEMBER _____

TODAY'S GOAL _____

POSITIVE AFFIRMATION _____

Dog Show Competition Log

SHOW DATE	NAME OF DOG/ARM BAND NUMBER	EVENT TYPE	NAME OF SHOW

CLASS ENTERED	PLACE IN CLASS	ENTRY IN CLASS	TOTAL ENTRY	POINTS	AWARD	GROUP	BEST IN SHOW

ENTRY BREAK DOWN_____RING #_____TIME_____BREEDS BEFORE_____

BREED JUDGE _____GROUP _____ BIS _____

AWARDS TODAY_____

POINTS COMING IN SHOW _____ POINTS EARNED TODAY _____ POINTS TO DATE _____

OTHER RESULTS/JUDGES (I.E. NOHS)_____

_____

NEW TITLE _____

COMMENTS AND TAKE-AWAYS

_____

_____

_____

_____

_____

SHOW PREPARATIONS AND FEES

SHOW ADDRESS/ETA _____

SHOW PHOTO TAKEN [YES] [NO] PHOTO SENT TO JUDGE [YES] [NO] PHOTOGRAPHER_____

FEES: ENTRY_____ PHOTOS_____ PARKING_____ GROOMING_____ HEALTH CLINICS_____

HANDLER NAME/FEE _____HEALTH CLINIC TIMES_____

HOTEL _____PET SITTER_____

THINGS TO REMEMBER _____

TODAY'S GOAL _____

POSITIVE AFFIRMATION _____

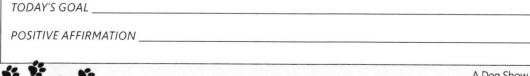

Dog Show Competition Log

SHOW DATE	NAME OF DOG/ARM BAND NUMBER	EVENT TYPE	NAME OF SHOW

CLASS ENTERED	PLACE IN CLASS	ENTRY IN CLASS	TOTAL ENTRY	POINTS	AWARD	GROUP	BEST IN SHOW

ENTRY BREAK DOWN_____RING #_____TIME_____BREEDS BEFORE_____

BREED JUDGE _____GROUP _____BIS _____

AWARDS TODAY_____

POINTS COMING IN SHOW _____ POINTS EARNED TODAY _____ POINTS TO DATE _____

OTHER RESULTS/JUDGES (I.E. NOHS)_____

_____

NEW TITLE _____

COMMENTS AND TAKE-AWAYS

_____

_____

_____

_____

_____

SHOW PREPARATIONS AND FEES

SHOW ADDRESS/ETA _____

SHOW PHOTO TAKEN [YES] [NO] PHOTO SENT TO JUDGE [YES] [NO] PHOTOGRAPHER_____

FEES: ENTRY_____ PHOTOS_____ PARKING_____ GROOMING_____ HEALTH CLINICS_____

HANDLER NAME/FEE _____HEALTH CLINIC TIMES_____

HOTEL _____PET SITTER_____

THINGS TO REMEMBER _____

TODAY'S GOAL _____

POSITIVE AFFIRMATION _____

Dog Show Competition Log

SHOW DATE	NAME OF DOG/ARM BAND NUMBER	EVENT TYPE	NAME OF SHOW

CLASS ENTERED	PLACE IN CLASS	ENTRY IN CLASS	TOTAL ENTRY	POINTS	AWARD	GROUP	BEST IN SHOW

ENTRY BREAK DOWN_____RING #_____TIME_____BREEDS BEFORE_____

BREED JUDGE _____GROUP _____BIS _____

AWARDS TODAY_____

POINTS COMING IN SHOW _____ POINTS EARNED TODAY _____ POINTS TO DATE _____

OTHER RESULTS/JUDGES (I.E. NOHS)_____

_____

NEW TITLE _____

COMMENTS AND TAKE-AWAYS

_____

_____

_____

_____

_____

SHOW PREPARATIONS AND FEES

SHOW ADDRESS/ETA _____

SHOW PHOTO TAKEN [YES] [NO] PHOTO SENT TO JUDGE [YES] [NO] PHOTOGRAPHER _____

FEES: ENTRY_____ PHOTOS_____ PARKING_____ GROOMING_____ HEALTH CLINICS_____

HANDLER NAME/FEE _____HEALTH CLINIC TIMES_____

HOTEL _____PET SITTER_____

THINGS TO REMEMBER _____

TODAY'S GOAL _____

POSITIVE AFFIRMATION _____

Dog Show Competition Log

SHOW DATE	NAME OF DOG/ARM BAND NUMBER	EVENT TYPE	NAME OF SHOW

CLASS ENTERED	PLACE IN CLASS	ENTRY IN CLASS	TOTAL ENTRY	POINTS	AWARD	GROUP	BEST IN SHOW

ENTRY BREAK DOWN_____RING #_____TIME_____BREEDS BEFORE_____

BREED JUDGE _____GROUP _____ BIS _____

AWARDS TODAY_____

POINTS COMING IN SHOW _____ POINTS EARNED TODAY _____ POINTS TO DATE _____

OTHER RESULTS/JUDGES (I.E. NOHS)_____

_____

NEW TITLE _____

COMMENTS AND TAKE-AWAYS

_____

_____

_____

_____

_____

SHOW PREPARATIONS AND FEES

SHOW ADDRESS/ETA _____

SHOW PHOTO TAKEN [YES] [NO] PHOTO SENT TO JUDGE [YES] [NO] PHOTOGRAPHER _____

FEES: ENTRY_____ PHOTOS_____ PARKING_____ GROOMING_____ HEALTH CLINICS_____

HANDLER NAME/FEE _____HEALTH CLINIC TIMES_____

HOTEL _____PET SITTER_____

THINGS TO REMEMBER _____

TODAY'S GOAL _____

POSITIVE AFFIRMATION _____

Dog Show Competition Log

SHOW DATE	NAME OF DOG/ARM BAND NUMBER	EVENT TYPE	NAME OF SHOW

CLASS ENTERED	PLACE IN CLASS	ENTRY IN CLASS	TOTAL ENTRY	POINTS	AWARD	GROUP	BEST IN SHOW

ENTRY BREAK DOWN_____RING #_____TIME_____BREEDS BEFORE_____

BREED JUDGE _____GROUP _____BIS _____

AWARDS TODAY_____

POINTS COMING IN SHOW _____ POINTS EARNED TODAY _____ POINTS TO DATE _____

OTHER RESULTS/JUDGES (I.E. NOHS)_____

_____

NEW TITLE _____

COMMENTS AND TAKE-AWAYS

_____

_____

_____

_____

_____

SHOW PREPARATIONS AND FEES

SHOW ADDRESS/ETA _____

SHOW PHOTO TAKEN [YES] [NO] PHOTO SENT TO JUDGE [YES] [NO] PHOTOGRAPHER _____

FEES: ENTRY_____ PHOTOS_____ PARKING_____ GROOMING_____ HEALTH CLINICS_____

HANDLER NAME/FEE _____HEALTH CLINIC TIMES_____

HOTEL _____PET SITTER_____

THINGS TO REMEMBER _____

TODAY'S GOAL _____

POSITIVE AFFIRMATION _____

Dog Show Competition Log

SHOW DATE	NAME OF DOG/ARM BAND NUMBER	EVENT TYPE	NAME OF SHOW

CLASS ENTERED	PLACE IN CLASS	ENTRY IN CLASS	TOTAL ENTRY	POINTS	AWARD	GROUP	BEST IN SHOW

ENTRY BREAK DOWN_____RING #_____TIME_____BREEDS BEFORE_____

BREED JUDGE _____GROUP _____BIS _____

AWARDS TODAY_____

POINTS COMING IN SHOW _____ POINTS EARNED TODAY _____ POINTS TO DATE _____

OTHER RESULTS/JUDGES (I.E. NOHS)_____

_____

NEW TITLE _____

COMMENTS AND TAKE-AWAYS

_____

_____

_____

_____

_____

SHOW PREPARATIONS AND FEES

SHOW ADDRESS/ETA _____

SHOW PHOTO TAKEN [YES] [NO] PHOTO SENT TO JUDGE [YES] [NO] PHOTOGRAPHER _____

FEES: ENTRY_____ PHOTOS_____ PARKING_____ GROOMING_____ HEALTH CLINICS_____

HANDLER NAME/FEE _____HEALTH CLINIC TIMES_____

HOTEL _____PET SITTER_____

THINGS TO REMEMBER _____

TODAY'S GOAL _____

POSITIVE AFFIRMATION _____

Dog Show Competition Log

SHOW DATE	NAME OF DOG/ARM BAND NUMBER	EVENT TYPE	NAME OF SHOW

CLASS ENTERED	PLACE IN CLASS	ENTRY IN CLASS	TOTAL ENTRY	POINTS	AWARD	GROUP	BEST IN SHOW

ENTRY BREAK DOWN_____RING #_____TIME_____BREEDS BEFORE_____

BREED JUDGE _____GROUP _____BIS _____

AWARDS TODAY_____

POINTS COMING IN SHOW _____ POINTS EARNED TODAY _____ POINTS TO DATE _____

OTHER RESULTS/JUDGES (I.E. NOHS)_____

_____

NEW TITLE _____

COMMENTS AND TAKE-AWAYS

_____

_____

_____

_____

_____

SHOW PREPARATIONS AND FEES

SHOW ADDRESS/ETA _____

SHOW PHOTO TAKEN [YES] [NO] PHOTO SENT TO JUDGE [YES] [NO] PHOTOGRAPHER_____

FEES: ENTRY_____ PHOTOS_____ PARKING_____ GROOMING_____ HEALTH CLINICS_____

HANDLER NAME/FEE _____HEALTH CLINIC TIMES_____

HOTEL _____PET SITTER_____

THINGS TO REMEMBER _____

TODAY'S GOAL _____

POSITIVE AFFIRMATION _____

Dog Show Competition Log

SHOW DATE	NAME OF DOG/ARM BAND NUMBER	EVENT TYPE	NAME OF SHOW

CLASS ENTERED	PLACE IN CLASS	ENTRY IN CLASS	TOTAL ENTRY	POINTS	AWARD	GROUP	BEST IN SHOW

ENTRY BREAK DOWN_____RING #_____TIME_____BREEDS BEFORE_____

BREED JUDGE _____GROUP _____ BIS _____

AWARDS TODAY_____

POINTS COMING IN SHOW _____ POINTS EARNED TODAY _____ POINTS TO DATE _____

OTHER RESULTS/JUDGES (I.E. NOHS)_____

_____

NEW TITLE _____

COMMENTS AND TAKE-AWAYS

_____

_____

_____

_____

_____

SHOW PREPARATIONS AND FEES

SHOW ADDRESS/ETA _____

SHOW PHOTO TAKEN [YES] [NO] PHOTO SENT TO JUDGE [YES] [NO] PHOTOGRAPHER_____

FEES: ENTRY_____ PHOTOS_____ PARKING_____ GROOMING_____ HEALTH CLINICS_____

HANDLER NAME/FEE _____HEALTH CLINIC TIMES_____

HOTEL _____PET SITTER_____

THINGS TO REMEMBER _____

TODAY'S GOAL _____

POSITIVE AFFIRMATION _____

Dog Show Competition Log

SHOW DATE	NAME OF DOG/ARM BAND NUMBER	EVENT TYPE	NAME OF SHOW

CLASS ENTERED	PLACE IN CLASS	ENTRY IN CLASS	TOTAL ENTRY	POINTS	AWARD	GROUP	BEST IN SHOW

ENTRY BREAK DOWN_____RING #_____TIME_____BREEDS BEFORE_____

BREED JUDGE _____GROUP _____ BIS _____

AWARDS TODAY_____

POINTS COMING IN SHOW _____ POINTS EARNED TODAY _____ POINTS TO DATE _____

OTHER RESULTS/JUDGES (I.E. NOHS)_____

_____

NEW TITLE _____

COMMENTS AND TAKE-AWAYS

_____

_____

_____

_____

_____

SHOW PREPARATIONS AND FEES

SHOW ADDRESS/ETA _____

SHOW PHOTO TAKEN ☐ YES ☐ NO PHOTO SENT TO JUDGE ☐ YES ☐ NO PHOTOGRAPHER _____

FEES: ENTRY_____ PHOTOS_____ PARKING_____ GROOMING_____ HEALTH CLINICS_____

HANDLER NAME/FEE _____HEALTH CLINIC TIMES_____

HOTEL _____PET SITTER_____

THINGS TO REMEMBER _____

TODAY'S GOAL _____

POSITIVE AFFIRMATION _____

Dog Show Competition Log

SHOW DATE	NAME OF DOG/ARM BAND NUMBER	EVENT TYPE	NAME OF SHOW

CLASS ENTERED	PLACE IN CLASS	ENTRY IN CLASS	TOTAL ENTRY	POINTS	AWARD	GROUP	BEST IN SHOW

ENTRY BREAK DOWN_____RING #_____TIME_____BREEDS BEFORE_____

BREED JUDGE _____GROUP _____BIS _____

AWARDS TODAY_____

POINTS COMING IN SHOW _____ POINTS EARNED TODAY _____ POINTS TO DATE _____

OTHER RESULTS/JUDGES (I.E. NOHS)_____

_____

NEW TITLE _____

COMMENTS AND TAKE-AWAYS

_____

_____

_____

_____

_____

SHOW PREPARATIONS AND FEES

SHOW ADDRESS/ETA _____

SHOW PHOTO TAKEN [YES] [NO] PHOTO SENT TO JUDGE [YES] [NO] PHOTOGRAPHER _____

FEES: ENTRY_____ PHOTOS_____ PARKING_____ GROOMING_____ HEALTH CLINICS_____

HANDLER NAME/FEE _____HEALTH CLINIC TIMES_____

HOTEL _____PET SITTER_____

THINGS TO REMEMBER _____

TODAY'S GOAL _____

POSITIVE AFFIRMATION _____

Dog Show Competition Log

SHOW DATE	NAME OF DOG/ARM BAND NUMBER	EVENT TYPE	NAME OF SHOW

CLASS ENTERED	PLACE IN CLASS	ENTRY IN CLASS	TOTAL ENTRY	POINTS	AWARD	GROUP	BEST IN SHOW

ENTRY BREAK DOWN_____RING #_____TIME_____BREEDS BEFORE_____

BREED JUDGE _____GROUP _____ BIS _____

AWARDS TODAY_____

POINTS COMING IN SHOW _____ POINTS EARNED TODAY _____ POINTS TO DATE _____

OTHER RESULTS/JUDGES (I.E. NOHS)_____

_____

NEW TITLE _____

COMMENTS AND TAKE-AWAYS

_____

_____

_____

_____

_____

SHOW PREPARATIONS AND FEES

SHOW ADDRESS/ETA _____

SHOW PHOTO TAKEN [YES] [NO] PHOTO SENT TO JUDGE [YES] [NO] PHOTOGRAPHER _____

FEES: ENTRY_____ PHOTOS_____ PARKING_____ GROOMING_____ HEALTH CLINICS_____

HANDLER NAME/FEE _____HEALTH CLINIC TIMES_____

HOTEL _____PET SITTER_____

THINGS TO REMEMBER _____

TODAY'S GOAL _____

POSITIVE AFFIRMATION _____

Dog Show Competition Log

SHOW DATE	NAME OF DOG/ARM BAND NUMBER	EVENT TYPE	NAME OF SHOW

CLASS ENTERED	PLACE IN CLASS	ENTRY IN CLASS	TOTAL ENTRY	POINTS	AWARD	GROUP	BEST IN SHOW

ENTRY BREAK DOWN_____RING #_____TIME_____BREEDS BEFORE_____

BREED JUDGE _____GROUP _____ BIS _____

AWARDS TODAY_____

POINTS COMING IN SHOW _____ POINTS EARNED TODAY _____ POINTS TO DATE _____

OTHER RESULTS/JUDGES (I.E. NOHS)_____

_____

NEW TITLE _____

COMMENTS AND TAKE-AWAYS

_____

_____

_____

_____

_____

SHOW PREPARATIONS AND FEES

SHOW ADDRESS/ETA _____

SHOW PHOTO TAKEN [YES] [NO] PHOTO SENT TO JUDGE [YES] [NO] PHOTOGRAPHER _____

FEES: ENTRY_____ PHOTOS_____ PARKING_____ GROOMING_____ HEALTH CLINICS_____

HANDLER NAME/FEE _____HEALTH CLINIC TIMES_____

HOTEL _____PET SITTER_____

THINGS TO REMEMBER _____

TODAY'S GOAL _____

POSITIVE AFFIRMATION _____

Dog Show Competition Log

SHOW DATE	NAME OF DOG/ARM BAND NUMBER	EVENT TYPE	NAME OF SHOW

CLASS ENTERED	PLACE IN CLASS	ENTRY IN CLASS	TOTAL ENTRY	POINTS	AWARD	GROUP	BEST IN SHOW

ENTRY BREAK DOWN_____RING #_____TIME_____BREEDS BEFORE_____

BREED JUDGE _____GROUP _____ BIS _____

AWARDS TODAY_____

POINTS COMING IN SHOW _____ POINTS EARNED TODAY _____ POINTS TO DATE _____

OTHER RESULTS/JUDGES (I.E. NOHS)_____

_____

NEW TITLE _____

COMMENTS AND TAKE-AWAYS

_____

_____

_____

_____

_____

SHOW PREPARATIONS AND FEES

SHOW ADDRESS/ETA _____

SHOW PHOTO TAKEN [YES] [NO] PHOTO SENT TO JUDGE [YES] [NO] PHOTOGRAPHER_____

FEES: ENTRY_____ PHOTOS_____ PARKING_____ GROOMING_____ HEALTH CLINICS_____

HANDLER NAME/FEE _____HEALTH CLINIC TIMES_____

HOTEL _____PET SITTER_____

THINGS TO REMEMBER _____

TODAY'S GOAL _____

POSITIVE AFFIRMATION _____

Dog Show Competition Log

SHOW DATE	NAME OF DOG/ARM BAND NUMBER	EVENT TYPE	NAME OF SHOW

CLASS ENTERED	PLACE IN CLASS	ENTRY IN CLASS	TOTAL ENTRY	POINTS	AWARD	GROUP	BEST IN SHOW

ENTRY BREAK DOWN_____RING #_____TIME_____BREEDS BEFORE_____

BREED JUDGE _____GROUP _____BIS _____

AWARDS TODAY_____

POINTS COMING IN SHOW _____ POINTS EARNED TODAY _____ POINTS TO DATE _____

OTHER RESULTS/JUDGES (I.E. NOHS)_____

_____

NEW TITLE _____

COMMENTS AND TAKE-AWAYS

_____

_____

_____

_____

_____

SHOW PREPARATIONS AND FEES

SHOW ADDRESS/ETA _____

SHOW PHOTO TAKEN [YES] [NO] PHOTO SENT TO JUDGE [YES] [NO] PHOTOGRAPHER _____

FEES: ENTRY_____ PHOTOS_____ PARKING_____ GROOMING_____ HEALTH CLINICS_____

HANDLER NAME/FEE _____HEALTH CLINIC TIMES_____

HOTEL _____PET SITTER_____

THINGS TO REMEMBER _____

TODAY'S GOAL _____

POSITIVE AFFIRMATION _____

Dog Show Competition Log

SHOW DATE	NAME OF DOG/ARM BAND NUMBER	EVENT TYPE	NAME OF SHOW

CLASS ENTERED	PLACE IN CLASS	ENTRY IN CLASS	TOTAL ENTRY	POINTS	AWARD	GROUP	BEST IN SHOW

ENTRY BREAK DOWN_____RING #_____TIME_____BREEDS BEFORE_____

BREED JUDGE _____GROUP _____ BIS _____

AWARDS TODAY_____

POINTS COMING IN SHOW _____ POINTS EARNED TODAY _____ POINTS TO DATE _____

OTHER RESULTS/JUDGES (I.E. NOHS)_____

_____

NEW TITLE _____

COMMENTS AND TAKE-AWAYS

_____

_____

_____

_____

_____

SHOW PREPARATIONS AND FEES

SHOW ADDRESS/ETA _____

SHOW PHOTO TAKEN [YES] [NO] PHOTO SENT TO JUDGE [YES] [NO] PHOTOGRAPHER _____

FEES: ENTRY_____ PHOTOS_____ PARKING_____ GROOMING_____ HEALTH CLINICS_____

HANDLER NAME/FEE _____HEALTH CLINIC TIMES_____

HOTEL _____PET SITTER_____

THINGS TO REMEMBER _____

TODAY'S GOAL _____

POSITIVE AFFIRMATION _____

Dog Show Competition Log

SHOW DATE	NAME OF DOG/ARM BAND NUMBER	EVENT TYPE	NAME OF SHOW

CLASS ENTERED	PLACE IN CLASS	ENTRY IN CLASS	TOTAL ENTRY	POINTS	AWARD	GROUP	BEST IN SHOW

ENTRY BREAK DOWN_____RING #_____TIME_____BREEDS BEFORE_____

BREED JUDGE _____GROUP _____ BIS _____

AWARDS TODAY_____

POINTS COMING IN SHOW _____ POINTS EARNED TODAY _____ POINTS TO DATE _____

OTHER RESULTS/JUDGES (I.E. NOHS)_____

_____

NEW TITLE _____

COMMENTS AND TAKE-AWAYS

_____

_____

_____

_____

_____

SHOW PREPARATIONS AND FEES

SHOW ADDRESS/ETA _____

SHOW PHOTO TAKEN [YES] [NO] PHOTO SENT TO JUDGE [YES] [NO] PHOTOGRAPHER _____

FEES: ENTRY_____ PHOTOS_____ PARKING_____ GROOMING_____ HEALTH CLINICS_____

HANDLER NAME/FEE _____HEALTH CLINIC TIMES_____

HOTEL _____PET SITTER_____

THINGS TO REMEMBER _____

TODAY'S GOAL _____

POSITIVE AFFIRMATION _____

Dog Show Competition Log

SHOW DATE	NAME OF DOG/ARM BAND NUMBER	EVENT TYPE	NAME OF SHOW

CLASS ENTERED	PLACE IN CLASS	ENTRY IN CLASS	TOTAL ENTRY	POINTS	AWARD	GROUP	BEST IN SHOW

ENTRY BREAK DOWN_____RING #_____TIME_____BREEDS BEFORE_____

BREED JUDGE _____GROUP _____BIS _____

AWARDS TODAY_____

POINTS COMING IN SHOW _____ POINTS EARNED TODAY _____ POINTS TO DATE _____

OTHER RESULTS/JUDGES (I.E. NOHS)_____

_____

NEW TITLE _____

COMMENTS AND TAKE-AWAYS

_____

_____

_____

_____

_____

SHOW PREPARATIONS AND FEES

SHOW ADDRESS/ETA _____

SHOW PHOTO TAKEN [YES] [NO] PHOTO SENT TO JUDGE [YES] [NO] PHOTOGRAPHER _____

FEES: ENTRY_____ PHOTOS_____ PARKING_____ GROOMING_____ HEALTH CLINICS_____

HANDLER NAME/FEE _____HEALTH CLINIC TIMES_____

HOTEL _____PET SITTER_____

THINGS TO REMEMBER _____

TODAY'S GOAL _____

POSITIVE AFFIRMATION _____

Dog Show Competition Log

SHOW DATE	NAME OF DOG/ARM BAND NUMBER	EVENT TYPE	NAME OF SHOW

CLASS ENTERED	PLACE IN CLASS	ENTRY IN CLASS	TOTAL ENTRY	POINTS	AWARD	GROUP	BEST IN SHOW

ENTRY BREAK DOWN_____RING #_____TIME_____BREEDS BEFORE_____

BREED JUDGE _____GROUP _____BIS _____

AWARDS TODAY_____

POINTS COMING IN SHOW _____ POINTS EARNED TODAY _____ POINTS TO DATE _____

OTHER RESULTS/JUDGES (I.E. NOHS)_____
_____

NEW TITLE _____

COMMENTS AND TAKE-AWAYS

_____
_____
_____
_____
_____

SHOW PREPARATIONS AND FEES

SHOW ADDRESS/ETA _____

SHOW PHOTO TAKEN [YES] [NO] PHOTO SENT TO JUDGE [YES] [NO] PHOTOGRAPHER _____

FEES: ENTRY_____ PHOTOS_____ PARKING_____ GROOMING_____ HEALTH CLINICS_____

HANDLER NAME/FEE _____HEALTH CLINIC TIMES_____

HOTEL _____PET SITTER_____

THINGS TO REMEMBER _____

TODAY'S GOAL _____

POSITIVE AFFIRMATION _____

Dog Show Competition Log

SHOW DATE	NAME OF DOG/ARM BAND NUMBER	EVENT TYPE	NAME OF SHOW

CLASS ENTERED	PLACE IN CLASS	ENTRY IN CLASS	TOTAL ENTRY	POINTS	AWARD	GROUP	BEST IN SHOW

ENTRY BREAK DOWN_____RING #_____TIME_____BREEDS BEFORE_____

BREED JUDGE _____GROUP _____BIS _____

AWARDS TODAY_____

POINTS COMING IN SHOW _____ POINTS EARNED TODAY _____ POINTS TO DATE _____

OTHER RESULTS/JUDGES (I.E. NOHS)_____

_____

NEW TITLE _____

COMMENTS AND TAKE-AWAYS

_____

_____

_____

_____

_____

SHOW PREPARATIONS AND FEES

SHOW ADDRESS/ETA _____

SHOW PHOTO TAKEN ☐ YES ☐ NO PHOTO SENT TO JUDGE ☐ YES ☐ NO PHOTOGRAPHER _____

FEES: ENTRY_____ PHOTOS_____ PARKING_____ GROOMING_____ HEALTH CLINICS_____

HANDLER NAME/FEE _____HEALTH CLINIC TIMES_____

HOTEL _____PET SITTER_____

THINGS TO REMEMBER _____

TODAY'S GOAL _____

POSITIVE AFFIRMATION _____

Dog Show Competition Log

SHOW DATE	NAME OF DOG/ARM BAND NUMBER	EVENT TYPE	NAME OF SHOW

CLASS ENTERED	PLACE IN CLASS	ENTRY IN CLASS	TOTAL ENTRY	POINTS	AWARD	GROUP	BEST IN SHOW

ENTRY BREAK DOWN_____RING #_____TIME_____BREEDS BEFORE_____

BREED JUDGE _____GROUP _____ BIS _____

AWARDS TODAY_____

POINTS COMING IN SHOW _____ POINTS EARNED TODAY _____ POINTS TO DATE _____

OTHER RESULTS/JUDGES (I.E. NOHS)_____

_____

NEW TITLE _____

COMMENTS AND TAKE-AWAYS

_____

_____

_____

_____

_____

SHOW PREPARATIONS AND FEES

SHOW ADDRESS/ETA _____

SHOW PHOTO TAKEN [YES] [NO] PHOTO SENT TO JUDGE [YES] [NO] PHOTOGRAPHER_____

FEES: ENTRY_____ PHOTOS_____ PARKING_____ GROOMING_____ HEALTH CLINICS_____

HANDLER NAME/FEE _____HEALTH CLINIC TIMES_____

HOTEL _____PET SITTER_____

THINGS TO REMEMBER _____

TODAY'S GOAL _____

POSITIVE AFFIRMATION _____

Dog Show Competition Log

SHOW DATE	NAME OF DOG/ARM BAND NUMBER	EVENT TYPE	NAME OF SHOW

CLASS ENTERED	PLACE IN CLASS	ENTRY IN CLASS	TOTAL ENTRY	POINTS	AWARD	GROUP	BEST IN SHOW

ENTRY BREAK DOWN_____RING #_____TIME_____BREEDS BEFORE_____

BREED JUDGE _____GROUP _____BIS _____

AWARDS TODAY_____

POINTS COMING IN SHOW _____ POINTS EARNED TODAY _____ POINTS TO DATE _____

OTHER RESULTS/JUDGES (I.E. NOHS)_____

_____

NEW TITLE _____

COMMENTS AND TAKE-AWAYS

_____

_____

_____

_____

_____

SHOW PREPARATIONS AND FEES

SHOW ADDRESS/ETA _____

SHOW PHOTO TAKEN [YES] [NO] PHOTO SENT TO JUDGE [YES] [NO] PHOTOGRAPHER _____

FEES: ENTRY_____ PHOTOS_____ PARKING_____ GROOMING_____ HEALTH CLINICS_____

HANDLER NAME/FEE _____HEALTH CLINIC TIMES_____

HOTEL _____PET SITTER_____

THINGS TO REMEMBER _____

TODAY'S GOAL _____

POSITIVE AFFIRMATION _____

Dog Show Competition Log

SHOW DATE	NAME OF DOG/ARM BAND NUMBER	EVENT TYPE	NAME OF SHOW

CLASS ENTERED	PLACE IN CLASS	ENTRY IN CLASS	TOTAL ENTRY	POINTS	AWARD	GROUP	BEST IN SHOW

ENTRY BREAK DOWN_____**RING #**_____**TIME**_____**BREEDS BEFORE**_____

BREED JUDGE _____GROUP _____BIS _____

AWARDS TODAY_____

POINTS COMING IN SHOW _____ POINTS EARNED TODAY _____ POINTS TO DATE _____

OTHER RESULTS/JUDGES (I.E. NOHS)_____

_____

NEW TITLE _____

COMMENTS AND TAKE-AWAYS

_____

_____

_____

_____

_____

SHOW PREPARATIONS AND FEES

SHOW ADDRESS/ETA _____

SHOW PHOTO TAKEN [YES] [NO] PHOTO SENT TO JUDGE [YES] [NO] PHOTOGRAPHER _____

FEES: ENTRY_____ PHOTOS_____ PARKING_____ GROOMING_____ HEALTH CLINICS_____

HANDLER NAME/FEE _____HEALTH CLINIC TIMES_____

HOTEL _____PET SITTER_____

THINGS TO REMEMBER _____

TODAY'S GOAL _____

POSITIVE AFFIRMATION _____

Dog Show Competition Log

SHOW DATE	NAME OF DOG/ARM BAND NUMBER	EVENT TYPE	NAME OF SHOW

CLASS ENTERED	PLACE IN CLASS	ENTRY IN CLASS	TOTAL ENTRY	POINTS	AWARD	GROUP	BEST IN SHOW

ENTRY BREAK DOWN_____RING #_____TIME_____BREEDS BEFORE_____

BREED JUDGE _____GROUP _____ BIS _____

AWARDS TODAY_____

POINTS COMING IN SHOW _____ POINTS EARNED TODAY _____ POINTS TO DATE _____

OTHER RESULTS/JUDGES (I.E. NOHS)_____

_____

NEW TITLE _____

COMMENTS AND TAKE-AWAYS

_____

_____

_____

_____

_____

SHOW PREPARATIONS AND FEES

SHOW ADDRESS/ETA _____

SHOW PHOTO TAKEN [YES] [NO] PHOTO SENT TO JUDGE [YES] [NO] PHOTOGRAPHER_____

FEES: ENTRY_____ PHOTOS_____ PARKING_____ GROOMING_____ HEALTH CLINICS_____

HANDLER NAME/FEE _____HEALTH CLINIC TIMES_____

HOTEL _____PET SITTER_____

THINGS TO REMEMBER _____

TODAY'S GOAL _____

POSITIVE AFFIRMATION _____

Dog Show Competition Log

SHOW DATE	NAME OF DOG/ARM BAND NUMBER	EVENT TYPE	NAME OF SHOW

CLASS ENTERED	PLACE IN CLASS	ENTRY IN CLASS	TOTAL ENTRY	POINTS	AWARD	GROUP	BEST IN SHOW

ENTRY BREAK DOWN_____RING #_____TIME_____BREEDS BEFORE_____

BREED JUDGE _____GROUP _____BIS _____

AWARDS TODAY_____

POINTS COMING IN SHOW _____ POINTS EARNED TODAY _____ POINTS TO DATE _____

OTHER RESULTS/JUDGES (I.E. NOHS)_____

_____

NEW TITLE _____

COMMENTS AND TAKE-AWAYS

_____

_____

_____

_____

_____

SHOW PREPARATIONS AND FEES

SHOW ADDRESS/ETA _____

SHOW PHOTO TAKEN [YES] [NO] PHOTO SENT TO JUDGE [YES] [NO] PHOTOGRAPHER_____

FEES: ENTRY_____ PHOTOS_____ PARKING_____ GROOMING_____ HEALTH CLINICS_____

HANDLER NAME/FEE _____HEALTH CLINIC TIMES_____

HOTEL _____PET SITTER_____

THINGS TO REMEMBER _____

TODAY'S GOAL _____

POSITIVE AFFIRMATION _____

Dog Show Competition Log

SHOW DATE	NAME OF DOG/ARM BAND NUMBER	EVENT TYPE	NAME OF SHOW

CLASS ENTERED	PLACE IN CLASS	ENTRY IN CLASS	TOTAL ENTRY	POINTS	AWARD	GROUP	BEST IN SHOW

ENTRY BREAK DOWN_____RING #_____TIME_____BREEDS BEFORE_____

BREED JUDGE _____GROUP _____BIS _____

AWARDS TODAY_____

POINTS COMING IN SHOW _____ POINTS EARNED TODAY _____ POINTS TO DATE _____

OTHER RESULTS/JUDGES (I.E. NOHS)_____

_____

NEW TITLE _____

COMMENTS AND TAKE-AWAYS

_____

_____

_____

_____

_____

SHOW PREPARATIONS AND FEES

SHOW ADDRESS/ETA _____

SHOW PHOTO TAKEN [YES] [NO] PHOTO SENT TO JUDGE [YES] [NO] PHOTOGRAPHER _____

FEES: ENTRY_____ PHOTOS_____ PARKING_____ GROOMING_____ HEALTH CLINICS_____

HANDLER NAME/FEE _____HEALTH CLINIC TIMES_____

HOTEL _____PET SITTER_____

THINGS TO REMEMBER _____

TODAY'S GOAL _____

POSITIVE AFFIRMATION _____

Dog Show Competition Log

SHOW DATE	NAME OF DOG/ARM BAND NUMBER	EVENT TYPE	NAME OF SHOW

CLASS ENTERED	PLACE IN CLASS	ENTRY IN CLASS	TOTAL ENTRY	POINTS	AWARD	GROUP	BEST IN SHOW

ENTRY BREAK DOWN_____RING #_____TIME_____BREEDS BEFORE_____

BREED JUDGE _____GROUP _____BIS _____

AWARDS TODAY_____

POINTS COMING IN SHOW _____ POINTS EARNED TODAY _____ POINTS TO DATE _____

OTHER RESULTS/JUDGES (I.E. NOHS)_____

_____

NEW TITLE _____

COMMENTS AND TAKE-AWAYS

_____

_____

_____

_____

_____

SHOW PREPARATIONS AND FEES

SHOW ADDRESS/ETA _____

SHOW PHOTO TAKEN [YES] [NO] PHOTO SENT TO JUDGE [YES] [NO] PHOTOGRAPHER _____

FEES: ENTRY_____ PHOTOS_____ PARKING_____ GROOMING_____ HEALTH CLINICS_____

HANDLER NAME/FEE _____HEALTH CLINIC TIMES_____

HOTEL _____PET SITTER_____

THINGS TO REMEMBER _____

TODAY'S GOAL _____

POSITIVE AFFIRMATION _____

Dog Show Competition Log

SHOW DATE	NAME OF DOG/ARM BAND NUMBER	EVENT TYPE	NAME OF SHOW

CLASS ENTERED	PLACE IN CLASS	ENTRY IN CLASS	TOTAL ENTRY	POINTS	AWARD	GROUP	BEST IN SHOW

ENTRY BREAK DOWN_____RING #_____TIME_____BREEDS BEFORE_____

BREED JUDGE _____GROUP _____BIS _____

AWARDS TODAY_____

POINTS COMING IN SHOW _____ POINTS EARNED TODAY _____ POINTS TO DATE _____

OTHER RESULTS/JUDGES (I.E. NOHS)_____

_____

NEW TITLE _____

COMMENTS AND TAKE-AWAYS

_____

_____

_____

_____

_____

SHOW PREPARATIONS AND FEES

SHOW ADDRESS/ETA _____

SHOW PHOTO TAKEN [YES] [NO] PHOTO SENT TO JUDGE [YES] [NO] PHOTOGRAPHER _____

FEES: ENTRY_____ PHOTOS_____ PARKING_____ GROOMING_____ HEALTH CLINICS_____

HANDLER NAME/FEE _____HEALTH CLINIC TIMES_____

HOTEL _____PET SITTER_____

THINGS TO REMEMBER _____

TODAY'S GOAL _____

POSITIVE AFFIRMATION _____

Dog Show Competition Log

SHOW DATE	NAME OF DOG/ARM BAND NUMBER	EVENT TYPE	NAME OF SHOW

CLASS ENTERED	PLACE IN CLASS	ENTRY IN CLASS	TOTAL ENTRY	POINTS	AWARD	GROUP	BEST IN SHOW

ENTRY BREAK DOWN_____RING #_____TIME_____BREEDS BEFORE_____

BREED JUDGE _____GROUP _____ BIS _____

AWARDS TODAY_____

POINTS COMING IN SHOW _____ POINTS EARNED TODAY _____ POINTS TO DATE _____

OTHER RESULTS/JUDGES (I.E. NOHS)_____

_____

NEW TITLE _____

COMMENTS AND TAKE-AWAYS

_____

_____

_____

_____

_____

SHOW PREPARATIONS AND FEES

SHOW ADDRESS/ETA _____

SHOW PHOTO TAKEN [YES] [NO] PHOTO SENT TO JUDGE [YES] [NO] PHOTOGRAPHER_____

FEES: ENTRY_____ PHOTOS_____ PARKING_____ GROOMING_____ HEALTH CLINICS_____

HANDLER NAME/FEE _____HEALTH CLINIC TIMES_____

HOTEL _____PET SITTER_____

THINGS TO REMEMBER _____

TODAY'S GOAL _____

POSITIVE AFFIRMATION _____

Dog Show Competition Log

SHOW DATE	NAME OF DOG/ARM BAND NUMBER	EVENT TYPE	NAME OF SHOW

CLASS ENTERED	PLACE IN CLASS	ENTRY IN CLASS	TOTAL ENTRY	POINTS	AWARD	GROUP	BEST IN SHOW

ENTRY BREAK DOWN_____RING #_____TIME_____BREEDS BEFORE_____

BREED JUDGE _____GROUP _____ BIS _____

AWARDS TODAY_____

POINTS COMING IN SHOW _____ POINTS EARNED TODAY _____ POINTS TO DATE _____

OTHER RESULTS/JUDGES (I.E. NOHS)_____

_____

NEW TITLE _____

COMMENTS AND TAKE-AWAYS

_____

_____

_____

_____

_____

SHOW PREPARATIONS AND FEES

SHOW ADDRESS/ETA _____

SHOW PHOTO TAKEN [YES] [NO] PHOTO SENT TO JUDGE [YES] [NO] PHOTOGRAPHER _____

FEES: ENTRY_____ PHOTOS_____ PARKING_____ GROOMING_____ HEALTH CLINICS_____

HANDLER NAME/FEE _____HEALTH CLINIC TIMES_____

HOTEL _____PET SITTER_____

THINGS TO REMEMBER _____

TODAY'S GOAL _____

POSITIVE AFFIRMATION _____

Dog Show Competition Log

SHOW DATE	NAME OF DOG/ARM BAND NUMBER	EVENT TYPE	NAME OF SHOW

CLASS ENTERED	PLACE IN CLASS	ENTRY IN CLASS	TOTAL ENTRY	POINTS	AWARD	GROUP	BEST IN SHOW

ENTRY BREAK DOWN_____RING #_____TIME_____BREEDS BEFORE_____

BREED JUDGE _____GROUP _____BIS _____

AWARDS TODAY_____

POINTS COMING IN SHOW _____ POINTS EARNED TODAY _____ POINTS TO DATE _____

OTHER RESULTS/JUDGES (I.E. NOHS)_____

_____

NEW TITLE _____

COMMENTS AND TAKE-AWAYS

_____

_____

_____

_____

_____

SHOW PREPARATIONS AND FEES

SHOW ADDRESS/ETA _____

SHOW PHOTO TAKEN [YES] [NO] PHOTO SENT TO JUDGE [YES] [NO] PHOTOGRAPHER_____

FEES: ENTRY_____ PHOTOS_____ PARKING_____ GROOMING_____ HEALTH CLINICS_____

HANDLER NAME/FEE _____HEALTH CLINIC TIMES_____

HOTEL _____PET SITTER_____

THINGS TO REMEMBER _____

TODAY'S GOAL _____

POSITIVE AFFIRMATION _____

Dog Show Competition Log

SHOW DATE	NAME OF DOG/ARM BAND NUMBER	EVENT TYPE	NAME OF SHOW

CLASS ENTERED	PLACE IN CLASS	ENTRY IN CLASS	TOTAL ENTRY	POINTS	AWARD	GROUP	BEST IN SHOW

ENTRY BREAK DOWN_____RING #_____TIME_____BREEDS BEFORE_____

BREED JUDGE _____GROUP _____BIS _____

AWARDS TODAY_____

POINTS COMING IN SHOW _____ POINTS EARNED TODAY _____ POINTS TO DATE _____

OTHER RESULTS/JUDGES (I.E. NOHS)_____

_____

NEW TITLE _____

COMMENTS AND TAKE-AWAYS

_____

_____

_____

_____

_____

SHOW PREPARATIONS AND FEES

SHOW ADDRESS/ETA _____

SHOW PHOTO TAKEN [YES] [NO] PHOTO SENT TO JUDGE [YES] [NO] PHOTOGRAPHER _____

FEES: ENTRY_____ PHOTOS_____ PARKING_____ GROOMING_____ HEALTH CLINICS_____

HANDLER NAME/FEE _____HEALTH CLINIC TIMES_____

HOTEL _____PET SITTER_____

THINGS TO REMEMBER _____

TODAY'S GOAL _____

POSITIVE AFFIRMATION _____

Dog Show Competition Log

SHOW DATE	NAME OF DOG/ARM BAND NUMBER	EVENT TYPE	NAME OF SHOW

CLASS ENTERED	PLACE IN CLASS	ENTRY IN CLASS	TOTAL ENTRY	POINTS	AWARD	GROUP	BEST IN SHOW

ENTRY BREAK DOWN_____RING #_____TIME_____BREEDS BEFORE_____

BREED JUDGE _____GROUP _____ BIS _____

AWARDS TODAY_____

POINTS COMING IN SHOW _____ POINTS EARNED TODAY _____ POINTS TO DATE _____

OTHER RESULTS/JUDGES (I.E. NOHS)_____

_____

NEW TITLE _____

COMMENTS AND TAKE-AWAYS

_____

_____

_____

_____

_____

SHOW PREPARATIONS AND FEES

SHOW ADDRESS/ETA _____

SHOW PHOTO TAKEN [YES] [NO] PHOTO SENT TO JUDGE [YES] [NO] PHOTOGRAPHER_____

FEES: ENTRY_____ PHOTOS_____ PARKING_____ GROOMING_____ HEALTH CLINICS_____

HANDLER NAME/FEE _____HEALTH CLINIC TIMES_____

HOTEL _____PET SITTER_____

THINGS TO REMEMBER _____

TODAY'S GOAL _____

POSITIVE AFFIRMATION _____

Dog Show Competition Log

SHOW DATE	NAME OF DOG/ARM BAND NUMBER	EVENT TYPE	NAME OF SHOW

CLASS ENTERED	PLACE IN CLASS	ENTRY IN CLASS	TOTAL ENTRY	POINTS	AWARD	GROUP	BEST IN SHOW

ENTRY BREAK DOWN_____RING #_____TIME_____BREEDS BEFORE_____

BREED JUDGE _____GROUP _____ BIS _____

AWARDS TODAY_____

POINTS COMING IN SHOW _____ POINTS EARNED TODAY _____ POINTS TO DATE _____

OTHER RESULTS/JUDGES (I.E. NOHS)_____

_____

NEW TITLE _____

COMMENTS AND TAKE-AWAYS

_____

_____

_____

_____

_____

SHOW PREPARATIONS AND FEES

SHOW ADDRESS/ETA _____

SHOW PHOTO TAKEN [YES] [NO] PHOTO SENT TO JUDGE [YES] [NO] PHOTOGRAPHER _____

FEES: ENTRY_____ PHOTOS_____ PARKING_____ GROOMING_____ HEALTH CLINICS_____

HANDLER NAME/FEE _____HEALTH CLINIC TIMES_____

HOTEL _____PET SITTER_____

THINGS TO REMEMBER _____

TODAY'S GOAL _____

POSITIVE AFFIRMATION _____

Dog Show Competition Log

SHOW DATE	NAME OF DOG/ARM BAND NUMBER	EVENT TYPE	NAME OF SHOW

CLASS ENTERED	PLACE IN CLASS	ENTRY IN CLASS	TOTAL ENTRY	POINTS	AWARD	GROUP	BEST IN SHOW

ENTRY BREAK DOWN_____RING #_____TIME_____BREEDS BEFORE_____

BREED JUDGE _____GROUP _____BIS _____

AWARDS TODAY_____

POINTS COMING IN SHOW _____ POINTS EARNED TODAY _____ POINTS TO DATE _____

OTHER RESULTS/JUDGES (I.E. NOHS)_____

_____

NEW TITLE _____

COMMENTS AND TAKE-AWAYS

_____

_____

_____

_____

_____

SHOW PREPARATIONS AND FEES

SHOW ADDRESS/ETA _____

SHOW PHOTO TAKEN [YES] [NO] PHOTO SENT TO JUDGE [YES] [NO] PHOTOGRAPHER _____

FEES: ENTRY_____ PHOTOS_____ PARKING_____ GROOMING_____ HEALTH CLINICS_____

HANDLER NAME/FEE _____HEALTH CLINIC TIMES_____

HOTEL _____PET SITTER_____

THINGS TO REMEMBER _____

TODAY'S GOAL _____

POSITIVE AFFIRMATION _____

Dog Show Competition Log

SHOW DATE	NAME OF DOG/ARM BAND NUMBER	EVENT TYPE	NAME OF SHOW

CLASS ENTERED	PLACE IN CLASS	ENTRY IN CLASS	TOTAL ENTRY	POINTS	AWARD	GROUP	BEST IN SHOW

ENTRY BREAK DOWN_____RING #_____TIME_____BREEDS BEFORE_____

BREED JUDGE _____GROUP _____BIS _____

AWARDS TODAY_____

POINTS COMING IN SHOW _____ POINTS EARNED TODAY _____ POINTS TO DATE _____

OTHER RESULTS/JUDGES (I.E. NOHS)_____

_____

NEW TITLE _____

COMMENTS AND TAKE-AWAYS

_____

_____

_____

_____

_____

SHOW PREPARATIONS AND FEES

SHOW ADDRESS/ETA _____

SHOW PHOTO TAKEN [YES] [NO] PHOTO SENT TO JUDGE [YES] [NO] PHOTOGRAPHER _____

FEES: ENTRY_____ PHOTOS_____ PARKING_____ GROOMING_____ HEALTH CLINICS_____

HANDLER NAME/FEE _____HEALTH CLINIC TIMES_____

HOTEL _____PET SITTER_____

THINGS TO REMEMBER _____

TODAY'S GOAL _____

POSITIVE AFFIRMATION _____

Dog Show Competition Log

SHOW DATE	NAME OF DOG/ARM BAND NUMBER	EVENT TYPE	NAME OF SHOW

CLASS ENTERED	PLACE IN CLASS	ENTRY IN CLASS	TOTAL ENTRY	POINTS	AWARD	GROUP	BEST IN SHOW

ENTRY BREAK DOWN_____RING #_____TIME_____BREEDS BEFORE_____

BREED JUDGE _____GROUP _____BIS _____

AWARDS TODAY_____

POINTS COMING IN SHOW _____ POINTS EARNED TODAY _____ POINTS TO DATE _____

OTHER RESULTS/JUDGES (I.E. NOHS)_____

_____

NEW TITLE _____

COMMENTS AND TAKE-AWAYS

_____

_____

_____

_____

_____

SHOW PREPARATIONS AND FEES

SHOW ADDRESS/ETA _____

SHOW PHOTO TAKEN [YES] [NO] PHOTO SENT TO JUDGE [YES] [NO] PHOTOGRAPHER _____

FEES: ENTRY_____ PHOTOS_____ PARKING_____ GROOMING_____ HEALTH CLINICS_____

HANDLER NAME/FEE _____HEALTH CLINIC TIMES_____

HOTEL _____PET SITTER_____

THINGS TO REMEMBER _____

TODAY'S GOAL _____

POSITIVE AFFIRMATION _____

Dog Show Competition Log

SHOW DATE	NAME OF DOG/ARM BAND NUMBER	EVENT TYPE	NAME OF SHOW

CLASS ENTERED	PLACE IN CLASS	ENTRY IN CLASS	TOTAL ENTRY	POINTS	AWARD	GROUP	BEST IN SHOW

ENTRY BREAK DOWN_____RING #_____TIME_____BREEDS BEFORE_____

BREED JUDGE _____GROUP _____BIS _____

AWARDS TODAY_____

POINTS COMING IN SHOW _____ POINTS EARNED TODAY _____ POINTS TO DATE _____

OTHER RESULTS/JUDGES (I.E. NOHS)_____

_____

NEW TITLE _____

COMMENTS AND TAKE-AWAYS

_____

_____

_____

_____

_____

SHOW PREPARATIONS AND FEES

SHOW ADDRESS/ETA _____

SHOW PHOTO TAKEN [YES] [NO] PHOTO SENT TO JUDGE [YES] [NO] PHOTOGRAPHER _____

FEES: ENTRY_____ PHOTOS_____ PARKING_____ GROOMING_____ HEALTH CLINICS_____

HANDLER NAME/FEE _____HEALTH CLINIC TIMES_____

HOTEL _____PET SITTER_____

THINGS TO REMEMBER _____

TODAY'S GOAL _____

POSITIVE AFFIRMATION _____

Dog Show Competition Log

SHOW DATE	NAME OF DOG/ARM BAND NUMBER	EVENT TYPE	NAME OF SHOW

CLASS ENTERED	PLACE IN CLASS	ENTRY IN CLASS	TOTAL ENTRY	POINTS	AWARD	GROUP	BEST IN SHOW

ENTRY BREAK DOWN_____RING #_____TIME_____BREEDS BEFORE_____

BREED JUDGE _____GROUP _____BIS _____

AWARDS TODAY_____

POINTS COMING IN SHOW _____ POINTS EARNED TODAY _____ POINTS TO DATE _____

OTHER RESULTS/JUDGES (I.E. NOHS)_____

_____

NEW TITLE _____

COMMENTS AND TAKE-AWAYS

_____

_____

_____

_____

_____

SHOW PREPARATIONS AND FEES

SHOW ADDRESS/ETA _____

SHOW PHOTO TAKEN [YES] [NO] PHOTO SENT TO JUDGE [YES] [NO] PHOTOGRAPHER _____

FEES: ENTRY_____ PHOTOS_____ PARKING_____ GROOMING_____ HEALTH CLINICS_____

HANDLER NAME/FEE _____HEALTH CLINIC TIMES_____

HOTEL _____PET SITTER_____

THINGS TO REMEMBER _____

TODAY'S GOAL _____

POSITIVE AFFIRMATION _____

Dog Show Competition Log

SHOW DATE	NAME OF DOG/ARM BAND NUMBER	EVENT TYPE	NAME OF SHOW

CLASS ENTERED	PLACE IN CLASS	ENTRY IN CLASS	TOTAL ENTRY	POINTS	AWARD	GROUP	BEST IN SHOW

ENTRY BREAK DOWN_____RING #_____TIME_____BREEDS BEFORE_____

BREED JUDGE _____GROUP _____BIS _____

AWARDS TODAY_____

POINTS COMING IN SHOW _____ POINTS EARNED TODAY _____ POINTS TO DATE _____

OTHER RESULTS/JUDGES (I.E. NOHS)_____

_____

NEW TITLE _____

COMMENTS AND TAKE-AWAYS

_____

_____

_____

_____

_____

SHOW PREPARATIONS AND FEES

SHOW ADDRESS/ETA _____

SHOW PHOTO TAKEN [YES] [NO] PHOTO SENT TO JUDGE [YES] [NO] PHOTOGRAPHER _____

FEES: ENTRY_____ PHOTOS_____ PARKING_____ GROOMING_____ HEALTH CLINICS_____

HANDLER NAME/FEE _____HEALTH CLINIC TIMES_____

HOTEL _____PET SITTER_____

THINGS TO REMEMBER _____

TODAY'S GOAL _____

POSITIVE AFFIRMATION _____

Dog Show Competition Log

SHOW DATE	NAME OF DOG/ARM BAND NUMBER	EVENT TYPE	NAME OF SHOW

CLASS ENTERED	PLACE IN CLASS	ENTRY IN CLASS	TOTAL ENTRY	POINTS	AWARD	GROUP	BEST IN SHOW

ENTRY BREAK DOWN_____RING #_____TIME_____BREEDS BEFORE_____

BREED JUDGE _____GROUP _____BIS _____

AWARDS TODAY_____

POINTS COMING IN SHOW _____ POINTS EARNED TODAY _____ POINTS TO DATE _____

OTHER RESULTS/JUDGES (I.E. NOHS)_____

_____

NEW TITLE _____

COMMENTS AND TAKE-AWAYS

_____

_____

_____

_____

_____

SHOW PREPARATIONS AND FEES

SHOW ADDRESS/ETA _____

SHOW PHOTO TAKEN [YES] [NO] PHOTO SENT TO JUDGE [YES] [NO] PHOTOGRAPHER_____

FEES: ENTRY_____ PHOTOS_____ PARKING_____ GROOMING_____ HEALTH CLINICS_____

HANDLER NAME/FEE _____HEALTH CLINIC TIMES_____

HOTEL _____PET SITTER_____

THINGS TO REMEMBER _____

TODAY'S GOAL _____

POSITIVE AFFIRMATION _____

Dog Show Competition Log

SHOW DATE	NAME OF DOG/ARM BAND NUMBER	EVENT TYPE	NAME OF SHOW

CLASS ENTERED	PLACE IN CLASS	ENTRY IN CLASS	TOTAL ENTRY	POINTS	AWARD	GROUP	BEST IN SHOW

ENTRY BREAK DOWN_____RING #_____TIME_____BREEDS BEFORE_____

BREED JUDGE _____GROUP _____BIS _____

AWARDS TODAY_____

POINTS COMING IN SHOW _____ POINTS EARNED TODAY _____ POINTS TO DATE _____

OTHER RESULTS/JUDGES (I.E. NOHS)_____

_____

NEW TITLE _____

COMMENTS AND TAKE-AWAYS

_____

_____

_____

_____

_____

SHOW PREPARATIONS AND FEES

SHOW ADDRESS/ETA _____

SHOW PHOTO TAKEN [YES] [NO] PHOTO SENT TO JUDGE [YES] [NO] PHOTOGRAPHER _____

FEES: ENTRY_____ PHOTOS_____ PARKING_____ GROOMING_____ HEALTH CLINICS_____

HANDLER NAME/FEE _____HEALTH CLINIC TIMES_____

HOTEL _____PET SITTER_____

THINGS TO REMEMBER _____

TODAY'S GOAL _____

POSITIVE AFFIRMATION _____

Dog Show Competition Log

SHOW DATE	NAME OF DOG/ARM BAND NUMBER	EVENT TYPE	NAME OF SHOW

CLASS ENTERED	PLACE IN CLASS	ENTRY IN CLASS	TOTAL ENTRY	POINTS	AWARD	GROUP	BEST IN SHOW

ENTRY BREAK DOWN_____RING #_____TIME_____BREEDS BEFORE_____

BREED JUDGE _____GROUP _____BIS _____

AWARDS TODAY_____

POINTS COMING IN SHOW _____ POINTS EARNED TODAY _____ POINTS TO DATE _____

OTHER RESULTS/JUDGES (I.E. NOHS)_____

_____

NEW TITLE _____

COMMENTS AND TAKE-AWAYS

_____

_____

_____

_____

_____

SHOW PREPARATIONS AND FEES

SHOW ADDRESS/ETA _____

SHOW PHOTO TAKEN [YES] [NO] PHOTO SENT TO JUDGE [YES] [NO] PHOTOGRAPHER _____

FEES: ENTRY_____ PHOTOS_____ PARKING_____ GROOMING_____ HEALTH CLINICS_____

HANDLER NAME/FEE _____HEALTH CLINIC TIMES_____

HOTEL _____PET SITTER_____

THINGS TO REMEMBER _____

TODAY'S GOAL _____

POSITIVE AFFIRMATION _____

Dog Show Competition Log

SHOW DATE	NAME OF DOG/ARM BAND NUMBER	EVENT TYPE	NAME OF SHOW

CLASS ENTERED	PLACE IN CLASS	ENTRY IN CLASS	TOTAL ENTRY	POINTS	AWARD	GROUP	BEST IN SHOW

ENTRY BREAK DOWN_____RING #_____TIME_____BREEDS BEFORE_____

BREED JUDGE _____GROUP _____BIS _____

AWARDS TODAY_____

POINTS COMING IN SHOW _____ POINTS EARNED TODAY _____ POINTS TO DATE _____

OTHER RESULTS/JUDGES (I.E. NOHS)_____

_____

NEW TITLE _____

COMMENTS AND TAKE-AWAYS

_____

_____

_____

_____

_____

SHOW PREPARATIONS AND FEES

SHOW ADDRESS/ETA _____

SHOW PHOTO TAKEN [YES] [NO] PHOTO SENT TO JUDGE [YES] [NO] PHOTOGRAPHER_____

FEES: ENTRY_____ PHOTOS_____ PARKING_____ GROOMING_____ HEALTH CLINICS_____

HANDLER NAME/FEE _____HEALTH CLINIC TIMES_____

HOTEL _____PET SITTER_____

THINGS TO REMEMBER _____

TODAY'S GOAL _____

POSITIVE AFFIRMATION _____

Dog Show Competition Log

SHOW DATE	NAME OF DOG/ARM BAND NUMBER	EVENT TYPE	NAME OF SHOW

CLASS ENTERED	PLACE IN CLASS	ENTRY IN CLASS	TOTAL ENTRY	POINTS	AWARD	GROUP	BEST IN SHOW

ENTRY BREAK DOWN_____RING #_____TIME_____BREEDS BEFORE_____

BREED JUDGE _____GROUP _____ BIS _____

AWARDS TODAY_____

POINTS COMING IN SHOW _____ POINTS EARNED TODAY _____ POINTS TO DATE _____

OTHER RESULTS/JUDGES (I.E. NOHS)_____

_____

NEW TITLE _____

COMMENTS AND TAKE-AWAYS

_____

_____

_____

_____

_____

SHOW PREPARATIONS AND FEES

SHOW ADDRESS/ETA _____

SHOW PHOTO TAKEN [YES] [NO] PHOTO SENT TO JUDGE [YES] [NO] PHOTOGRAPHER_____

FEES: ENTRY_____ PHOTOS_____ PARKING_____ GROOMING_____ HEALTH CLINICS_____

HANDLER NAME/FEE _____HEALTH CLINIC TIMES_____

HOTEL _____PET SITTER_____

THINGS TO REMEMBER _____

TODAY'S GOAL _____

POSITIVE AFFIRMATION _____

Dog Show Competition Log

SHOW DATE	NAME OF DOG/ARM BAND NUMBER	EVENT TYPE	NAME OF SHOW

CLASS ENTERED	PLACE IN CLASS	ENTRY IN CLASS	TOTAL ENTRY	POINTS	AWARD	GROUP	BEST IN SHOW

ENTRY BREAK DOWN_____RING #_____TIME_____BREEDS BEFORE_____

BREED JUDGE _____GROUP _____BIS _____

AWARDS TODAY_____

POINTS COMING IN SHOW _____ POINTS EARNED TODAY _____ POINTS TO DATE _____

OTHER RESULTS/JUDGES (I.E. NOHS)_____

_____

NEW TITLE _____

COMMENTS AND TAKE-AWAYS

_____

_____

_____

_____

_____

SHOW PREPARATIONS AND FEES

SHOW ADDRESS/ETA _____

SHOW PHOTO TAKEN [YES] [NO] PHOTO SENT TO JUDGE [YES] [NO] PHOTOGRAPHER _____

FEES: ENTRY_____ PHOTOS_____ PARKING_____ GROOMING_____ HEALTH CLINICS_____

HANDLER NAME/FEE _____HEALTH CLINIC TIMES_____

HOTEL _____PET SITTER_____

THINGS TO REMEMBER _____

TODAY'S GOAL _____

POSITIVE AFFIRMATION _____

Dog Show Competition Log

SHOW DATE	NAME OF DOG/ARM BAND NUMBER	EVENT TYPE	NAME OF SHOW

CLASS ENTERED	PLACE IN CLASS	ENTRY IN CLASS	TOTAL ENTRY	POINTS	AWARD	GROUP	BEST IN SHOW

ENTRY BREAK DOWN_____RING #_____TIME_____BREEDS BEFORE_____

BREED JUDGE _____GROUP _____BIS _____

AWARDS TODAY_____

POINTS COMING IN SHOW _____ POINTS EARNED TODAY _____ POINTS TO DATE _____

OTHER RESULTS/JUDGES (I.E. NOHS)_____

_____

NEW TITLE _____

COMMENTS AND TAKE-AWAYS

_____

_____

_____

_____

_____

SHOW PREPARATIONS AND FEES

SHOW ADDRESS/ETA _____

SHOW PHOTO TAKEN [YES] [NO] PHOTO SENT TO JUDGE [YES] [NO] PHOTOGRAPHER _____

FEES: ENTRY_____ PHOTOS_____ PARKING_____ GROOMING_____ HEALTH CLINICS_____

HANDLER NAME/FEE _____HEALTH CLINIC TIMES_____

HOTEL _____PET SITTER_____

THINGS TO REMEMBER _____

TODAY'S GOAL _____

POSITIVE AFFIRMATION _____

Dog Show Competition Log

SHOW DATE	NAME OF DOG/ARM BAND NUMBER	EVENT TYPE	NAME OF SHOW

CLASS ENTERED	PLACE IN CLASS	ENTRY IN CLASS	TOTAL ENTRY	POINTS	AWARD	GROUP	BEST IN SHOW

ENTRY BREAK DOWN_____RING #_____TIME_____BREEDS BEFORE_____

BREED JUDGE _____GROUP _____BIS _____

AWARDS TODAY_____

POINTS COMING IN SHOW _____ POINTS EARNED TODAY _____ POINTS TO DATE _____

OTHER RESULTS/JUDGES (I.E. NOHS)_____

_____

NEW TITLE _____

COMMENTS AND TAKE-AWAYS

_____

_____

_____

_____

_____

SHOW PREPARATIONS AND FEES

SHOW ADDRESS/ETA _____

SHOW PHOTO TAKEN ⬜ YES ⬜ NO PHOTO SENT TO JUDGE ⬜ YES ⬜ NO PHOTOGRAPHER _____

FEES: ENTRY_____ PHOTOS_____ PARKING_____ GROOMING_____ HEALTH CLINICS_____

HANDLER NAME/FEE _____HEALTH CLINIC TIMES_____

HOTEL _____PET SITTER_____

THINGS TO REMEMBER _____

TODAY'S GOAL _____

POSITIVE AFFIRMATION _____

Dog Show Competition Log

SHOW DATE	NAME OF DOG/ARM BAND NUMBER	EVENT TYPE	NAME OF SHOW

CLASS ENTERED	PLACE IN CLASS	ENTRY IN CLASS	TOTAL ENTRY	POINTS	AWARD	GROUP	BEST IN SHOW

ENTRY BREAK DOWN_____RING #_____TIME_____BREEDS BEFORE_____

BREED JUDGE _____GROUP _____ BIS _____

AWARDS TODAY_____

POINTS COMING IN SHOW _____ POINTS EARNED TODAY _____ POINTS TO DATE _____

OTHER RESULTS/JUDGES (I.E. NOHS)_____

_____

NEW TITLE _____

COMMENTS AND TAKE-AWAYS

_____

_____

_____

_____

_____

SHOW PREPARATIONS AND FEES

SHOW ADDRESS/ETA _____

SHOW PHOTO TAKEN [YES] [NO] PHOTO SENT TO JUDGE [YES] [NO] PHOTOGRAPHER_____

FEES: ENTRY_____ PHOTOS_____ PARKING_____ GROOMING_____ HEALTH CLINICS_____

HANDLER NAME/FEE _____HEALTH CLINIC TIMES_____

HOTEL _____PET SITTER_____

THINGS TO REMEMBER _____

TODAY'S GOAL _____

POSITIVE AFFIRMATION _____

Dog Show Competition Log

SHOW DATE	NAME OF DOG/ARM BAND NUMBER	EVENT TYPE	NAME OF SHOW

CLASS ENTERED	PLACE IN CLASS	ENTRY IN CLASS	TOTAL ENTRY	POINTS	AWARD	GROUP	BEST IN SHOW

ENTRY BREAK DOWN_____RING #_____TIME_____BREEDS BEFORE_____

BREED JUDGE _____GROUP _____ BIS _____

AWARDS TODAY_____

POINTS COMING IN SHOW _____ POINTS EARNED TODAY _____ POINTS TO DATE _____

OTHER RESULTS/JUDGES (I.E. NOHS)_____

_____

NEW TITLE _____

COMMENTS AND TAKE-AWAYS

_____

_____

_____

_____

_____

SHOW PREPARATIONS AND FEES

SHOW ADDRESS/ETA _____

SHOW PHOTO TAKEN [YES] [NO] PHOTO SENT TO JUDGE [YES] [NO] PHOTOGRAPHER_____

FEES: ENTRY_____ PHOTOS_____ PARKING_____ GROOMING_____ HEALTH CLINICS_____

HANDLER NAME/FEE _____HEALTH CLINIC TIMES_____

HOTEL _____PET SITTER_____

THINGS TO REMEMBER _____

TODAY'S GOAL _____

POSITIVE AFFIRMATION _____

Dog Show Competition Log

SHOW DATE	NAME OF DOG/ARM BAND NUMBER	EVENT TYPE	NAME OF SHOW

CLASS ENTERED	PLACE IN CLASS	ENTRY IN CLASS	TOTAL ENTRY	POINTS	AWARD	GROUP	BEST IN SHOW

ENTRY BREAK DOWN_____RING #_____TIME_____BREEDS BEFORE_____

BREED JUDGE _____GROUP _____BIS _____

AWARDS TODAY_____

POINTS COMING IN SHOW _____ POINTS EARNED TODAY _____ POINTS TO DATE _____

OTHER RESULTS/JUDGES (I.E. NOHS)_____

_____

NEW TITLE _____

COMMENTS AND TAKE-AWAYS

_____

_____

_____

_____

_____

SHOW PREPARATIONS AND FEES

SHOW ADDRESS/ETA _____

SHOW PHOTO TAKEN [YES] [NO] PHOTO SENT TO JUDGE [YES] [NO] PHOTOGRAPHER_____

FEES: ENTRY_____ PHOTOS_____ PARKING_____ GROOMING_____ HEALTH CLINICS_____

HANDLER NAME/FEE _____HEALTH CLINIC TIMES_____

HOTEL _____PET SITTER_____

THINGS TO REMEMBER _____

TODAY'S GOAL _____

POSITIVE AFFIRMATION _____

Dog Show Competition Log

SHOW DATE	NAME OF DOG/ARM BAND NUMBER	EVENT TYPE	NAME OF SHOW

CLASS ENTERED	PLACE IN CLASS	ENTRY IN CLASS	TOTAL ENTRY	POINTS	AWARD	GROUP	BEST IN SHOW

ENTRY BREAK DOWN_____RING #_____TIME_____BREEDS BEFORE_____

BREED JUDGE _____GROUP _____BIS _____

AWARDS TODAY_____

POINTS COMING IN SHOW _____ POINTS EARNED TODAY _____ POINTS TO DATE _____

OTHER RESULTS/JUDGES (I.E. NOHS)_____

_____

NEW TITLE _____

COMMENTS AND TAKE-AWAYS

_____

_____

_____

_____

_____

SHOW PREPARATIONS AND FEES

SHOW ADDRESS/ETA _____

SHOW PHOTO TAKEN [YES] [NO] PHOTO SENT TO JUDGE [YES] [NO] PHOTOGRAPHER _____

FEES: ENTRY_____ PHOTOS_____ PARKING_____ GROOMING_____ HEALTH CLINICS_____

HANDLER NAME/FEE _____HEALTH CLINIC TIMES_____

HOTEL _____PET SITTER_____

THINGS TO REMEMBER _____

TODAY'S GOAL _____

POSITIVE AFFIRMATION _____

Dog Show Competition Log

SHOW DATE	NAME OF DOG/ARM BAND NUMBER	EVENT TYPE	NAME OF SHOW

CLASS ENTERED	PLACE IN CLASS	ENTRY IN CLASS	TOTAL ENTRY	POINTS	AWARD	GROUP	BEST IN SHOW

ENTRY BREAK DOWN_____RING #_____TIME_____BREEDS BEFORE_____

BREED JUDGE _____GROUP _____ BIS _____

AWARDS TODAY_____

POINTS COMING IN SHOW _____ POINTS EARNED TODAY _____ POINTS TO DATE _____

OTHER RESULTS/JUDGES (I.E. NOHS)_____

_____

NEW TITLE _____

COMMENTS AND TAKE-AWAYS

_____

_____

_____

_____

_____

SHOW PREPARATIONS AND FEES

SHOW ADDRESS/ETA _____

SHOW PHOTO TAKEN [YES] [NO] PHOTO SENT TO JUDGE [YES] [NO] PHOTOGRAPHER_____

FEES: ENTRY_____ PHOTOS_____ PARKING_____ GROOMING_____ HEALTH CLINICS_____

HANDLER NAME/FEE _____HEALTH CLINIC TIMES_____

HOTEL _____PET SITTER_____

THINGS TO REMEMBER _____

TODAY'S GOAL _____

POSITIVE AFFIRMATION _____

Dog Show Competition Log

SHOW DATE	NAME OF DOG/ARM BAND NUMBER	EVENT TYPE	NAME OF SHOW

CLASS ENTERED	PLACE IN CLASS	ENTRY IN CLASS	TOTAL ENTRY	POINTS	AWARD	GROUP	BEST IN SHOW

ENTRY BREAK DOWN_____RING #_____TIME_____BREEDS BEFORE_____

BREED JUDGE _____GROUP _____ BIS _____

AWARDS TODAY_____

POINTS COMING IN SHOW _____ POINTS EARNED TODAY _____ POINTS TO DATE _____

OTHER RESULTS/JUDGES (I.E. NOHS)_____

_____

NEW TITLE _____

COMMENTS AND TAKE-AWAYS

_____

_____

_____

_____

_____

SHOW PREPARATIONS AND FEES

SHOW ADDRESS/ETA _____

SHOW PHOTO TAKEN [YES] [NO] PHOTO SENT TO JUDGE [YES] [NO] PHOTOGRAPHER _____

FEES: ENTRY_____ PHOTOS_____ PARKING_____ GROOMING_____ HEALTH CLINICS_____

HANDLER NAME/FEE _____HEALTH CLINIC TIMES_____

HOTEL _____PET SITTER_____

THINGS TO REMEMBER _____

TODAY'S GOAL _____

POSITIVE AFFIRMATION _____

Dog Show Competition Log

SHOW DATE	NAME OF DOG/ARM BAND NUMBER	EVENT TYPE	NAME OF SHOW

CLASS ENTERED	PLACE IN CLASS	ENTRY IN CLASS	TOTAL ENTRY	POINTS	AWARD	GROUP	BEST IN SHOW

ENTRY BREAK DOWN_____RING #_____TIME_____BREEDS BEFORE_____

BREED JUDGE _____GROUP _____ BIS _____

AWARDS TODAY_____

POINTS COMING IN SHOW _____ POINTS EARNED TODAY _____ POINTS TO DATE _____

OTHER RESULTS/JUDGES (I.E. NOHS)_____

_____

NEW TITLE _____

COMMENTS AND TAKE-AWAYS

_____

_____

_____

_____

_____

SHOW PREPARATIONS AND FEES

SHOW ADDRESS/ETA _____

SHOW PHOTO TAKEN [YES] [NO] PHOTO SENT TO JUDGE [YES] [NO] PHOTOGRAPHER _____

FEES: ENTRY_____ PHOTOS_____ PARKING_____ GROOMING_____ HEALTH CLINICS_____

HANDLER NAME/FEE _____HEALTH CLINIC TIMES_____

HOTEL _____PET SITTER_____

THINGS TO REMEMBER _____

TODAY'S GOAL _____

POSITIVE AFFIRMATION _____

Dog Show Competition Log

SHOW DATE	NAME OF DOG/ARM BAND NUMBER	EVENT TYPE	NAME OF SHOW

CLASS ENTERED	PLACE IN CLASS	ENTRY IN CLASS	TOTAL ENTRY	POINTS	AWARD	GROUP	BEST IN SHOW

ENTRY BREAK DOWN_____RING #_____TIME_____BREEDS BEFORE_____

BREED JUDGE _____GROUP _____BIS _____

AWARDS TODAY_____

POINTS COMING IN SHOW _____ POINTS EARNED TODAY _____ POINTS TO DATE _____

OTHER RESULTS/JUDGES (I.E. NOHS)_____

_____

NEW TITLE _____

COMMENTS AND TAKE-AWAYS

_____

_____

_____

_____

_____

SHOW PREPARATIONS AND FEES

SHOW ADDRESS/ETA _____

SHOW PHOTO TAKEN [YES] [NO] PHOTO SENT TO JUDGE [YES] [NO] PHOTOGRAPHER _____

FEES: ENTRY_____ PHOTOS_____ PARKING_____ GROOMING_____ HEALTH CLINICS_____

HANDLER NAME/FEE _____HEALTH CLINIC TIMES_____

HOTEL _____PET SITTER_____

THINGS TO REMEMBER _____

TODAY'S GOAL _____

POSITIVE AFFIRMATION _____

Dog Show Competition Log

SHOW DATE	NAME OF DOG/ARM BAND NUMBER	EVENT TYPE	NAME OF SHOW

CLASS ENTERED	PLACE IN CLASS	ENTRY IN CLASS	TOTAL ENTRY	POINTS	AWARD	GROUP	BEST IN SHOW

ENTRY BREAK DOWN_____RING #_____TIME_____BREEDS BEFORE_____

BREED JUDGE _____GROUP _____ BIS _____

AWARDS TODAY_____

POINTS COMING IN SHOW _____ POINTS EARNED TODAY _____ POINTS TO DATE _____

OTHER RESULTS/JUDGES (I.E. NOHS)_____

_____

NEW TITLE _____

COMMENTS AND TAKE-AWAYS

_____

_____

_____

_____

_____

SHOW PREPARATIONS AND FEES

SHOW ADDRESS/ETA _____

SHOW PHOTO TAKEN [YES] [NO] PHOTO SENT TO JUDGE [YES] [NO] PHOTOGRAPHER_____

FEES: ENTRY_____ PHOTOS_____ PARKING_____ GROOMING_____ HEALTH CLINICS_____

HANDLER NAME/FEE _____HEALTH CLINIC TIMES_____

HOTEL _____PET SITTER_____

THINGS TO REMEMBER _____

TODAY'S GOAL _____

POSITIVE AFFIRMATION _____

Dog Show Competition Log

SHOW DATE	NAME OF DOG/ARM BAND NUMBER	EVENT TYPE	NAME OF SHOW

CLASS ENTERED	PLACE IN CLASS	ENTRY IN CLASS	TOTAL ENTRY	POINTS	AWARD	GROUP	BEST IN SHOW

ENTRY BREAK DOWN_____RING #_____TIME_____BREEDS BEFORE_____

BREED JUDGE _____GROUP _____ BIS _____

AWARDS TODAY_____

POINTS COMING IN SHOW _____ POINTS EARNED TODAY _____ POINTS TO DATE _____

OTHER RESULTS/JUDGES (I.E. NOHS)_____

_____

NEW TITLE _____

COMMENTS AND TAKE-AWAYS

_____

_____

_____

_____

_____

SHOW PREPARATIONS AND FEES

SHOW ADDRESS/ETA _____

SHOW PHOTO TAKEN [YES] [NO] PHOTO SENT TO JUDGE [YES] [NO] PHOTOGRAPHER_____

FEES: ENTRY_____ PHOTOS_____ PARKING_____ GROOMING_____ HEALTH CLINICS_____

HANDLER NAME/FEE _____HEALTH CLINIC TIMES_____

HOTEL _____PET SITTER_____

THINGS TO REMEMBER _____

TODAY'S GOAL _____

POSITIVE AFFIRMATION _____

Dog Show Competition Log

SHOW DATE	NAME OF DOG/ARM BAND NUMBER	EVENT TYPE	NAME OF SHOW

CLASS ENTERED	PLACE IN CLASS	ENTRY IN CLASS	TOTAL ENTRY	POINTS	AWARD	GROUP	BEST IN SHOW

ENTRY BREAK DOWN_____RING #_____TIME_____BREEDS BEFORE_____

BREED JUDGE _____GROUP _____BIS _____

AWARDS TODAY_____

POINTS COMING IN SHOW _____ POINTS EARNED TODAY _____ POINTS TO DATE _____

OTHER RESULTS/JUDGES (I.E. NOHS)_____

_____

NEW TITLE _____

COMMENTS AND TAKE-AWAYS

_____

_____

_____

_____

_____

SHOW PREPARATIONS AND FEES

SHOW ADDRESS/ETA _____

SHOW PHOTO TAKEN [YES] [NO] PHOTO SENT TO JUDGE [YES] [NO] PHOTOGRAPHER _____

FEES: ENTRY_____ PHOTOS_____ PARKING_____ GROOMING_____ HEALTH CLINICS_____

HANDLER NAME/FEE _____HEALTH CLINIC TIMES_____

HOTEL _____PET SITTER_____

THINGS TO REMEMBER _____

TODAY'S GOAL _____

POSITIVE AFFIRMATION _____

Dog Show Competition Log

SHOW DATE	NAME OF DOG/ARM BAND NUMBER	EVENT TYPE	NAME OF SHOW

CLASS ENTERED	PLACE IN CLASS	ENTRY IN CLASS	TOTAL ENTRY	POINTS	AWARD	GROUP	BEST IN SHOW

ENTRY BREAK DOWN_____RING #_____TIME_____BREEDS BEFORE_____

BREED JUDGE _____GROUP _____BIS _____

AWARDS TODAY_____

POINTS COMING IN SHOW _____ POINTS EARNED TODAY _____ POINTS TO DATE _____

OTHER RESULTS/JUDGES (I.E. NOHS)_____

_____

NEW TITLE _____

COMMENTS AND TAKE-AWAYS

_____

_____

_____

_____

_____

SHOW PREPARATIONS AND FEES

SHOW ADDRESS/ETA _____

SHOW PHOTO TAKEN [YES] [NO] PHOTO SENT TO JUDGE [YES] [NO] PHOTOGRAPHER _____

FEES: ENTRY_____ PHOTOS_____ PARKING_____ GROOMING_____ HEALTH CLINICS_____

HANDLER NAME/FEE _____HEALTH CLINIC TIMES_____

HOTEL _____PET SITTER_____

THINGS TO REMEMBER _____

TODAY'S GOAL _____

POSITIVE AFFIRMATION _____

Dog Show Competition Log

SHOW DATE	NAME OF DOG/ARM BAND NUMBER	EVENT TYPE	NAME OF SHOW

CLASS ENTERED	PLACE IN CLASS	ENTRY IN CLASS	TOTAL ENTRY	POINTS	AWARD	GROUP	BEST IN SHOW

ENTRY BREAK DOWN_____RING #_____TIME_____BREEDS BEFORE_____

BREED JUDGE _____GROUP _____ BIS _____

AWARDS TODAY_____

POINTS COMING IN SHOW _____ POINTS EARNED TODAY _____ POINTS TO DATE _____

OTHER RESULTS/JUDGES (I.E. NOHS)_____

_____

NEW TITLE _____

COMMENTS AND TAKE-AWAYS

_____

_____

_____

_____

_____

SHOW PREPARATIONS AND FEES

SHOW ADDRESS/ETA _____

SHOW PHOTO TAKEN [YES] [NO] PHOTO SENT TO JUDGE [YES] [NO] PHOTOGRAPHER_____

FEES: ENTRY_____ PHOTOS_____ PARKING_____ GROOMING_____ HEALTH CLINICS_____

HANDLER NAME/FEE _____HEALTH CLINIC TIMES_____

HOTEL _____PET SITTER_____

THINGS TO REMEMBER _____

TODAY'S GOAL _____

POSITIVE AFFIRMATION _____

Dog Show Competition Log

SHOW DATE	NAME OF DOG/ARM BAND NUMBER	EVENT TYPE	NAME OF SHOW

CLASS ENTERED	PLACE IN CLASS	ENTRY IN CLASS	TOTAL ENTRY	POINTS	AWARD	GROUP	BEST IN SHOW

ENTRY BREAK DOWN_____RING #_____TIME_____BREEDS BEFORE_____

BREED JUDGE _____GROUP _____BIS _____

AWARDS TODAY_____

POINTS COMING IN SHOW _____ POINTS EARNED TODAY _____ POINTS TO DATE _____

OTHER RESULTS/JUDGES (I.E. NOHS)_____

_____

NEW TITLE _____

COMMENTS AND TAKE-AWAYS

_____

_____

_____

_____

_____

SHOW PREPARATIONS AND FEES

SHOW ADDRESS/ETA _____

SHOW PHOTO TAKEN [YES] [NO] PHOTO SENT TO JUDGE [YES] [NO] PHOTOGRAPHER_____

FEES: ENTRY_____ PHOTOS_____ PARKING_____ GROOMING_____ HEALTH CLINICS_____

HANDLER NAME/FEE _____HEALTH CLINIC TIMES_____

HOTEL _____PET SITTER_____

THINGS TO REMEMBER _____

TODAY'S GOAL _____

POSITIVE AFFIRMATION _____

Dog Show Competition Log

SHOW DATE	NAME OF DOG/ARM BAND NUMBER	EVENT TYPE	NAME OF SHOW

CLASS ENTERED	PLACE IN CLASS	ENTRY IN CLASS	TOTAL ENTRY	POINTS	AWARD	GROUP	BEST IN SHOW

ENTRY BREAK DOWN_____RING #_____TIME_____BREEDS BEFORE_____

BREED JUDGE _____GROUP _____BIS _____

AWARDS TODAY_____

POINTS COMING IN SHOW _____ POINTS EARNED TODAY _____ POINTS TO DATE _____

OTHER RESULTS/JUDGES (I.E. NOHS)_____

_____

NEW TITLE _____

COMMENTS AND TAKE-AWAYS

_____

_____

_____

_____

_____

SHOW PREPARATIONS AND FEES

SHOW ADDRESS/ETA _____

SHOW PHOTO TAKEN [YES] [NO] PHOTO SENT TO JUDGE [YES] [NO] PHOTOGRAPHER _____

FEES: ENTRY_____ PHOTOS_____ PARKING_____ GROOMING_____ HEALTH CLINICS_____

HANDLER NAME/FEE _____HEALTH CLINIC TIMES_____

HOTEL _____PET SITTER_____

THINGS TO REMEMBER _____

TODAY'S GOAL _____

POSITIVE AFFIRMATION _____

Dog Show Competition Log

SHOW DATE	NAME OF DOG/ARM BAND NUMBER	EVENT TYPE	NAME OF SHOW

CLASS ENTERED	PLACE IN CLASS	ENTRY IN CLASS	TOTAL ENTRY	POINTS	AWARD	GROUP	BEST IN SHOW

ENTRY BREAK DOWN_____RING #_____TIME_____BREEDS BEFORE_____

BREED JUDGE _____GROUP _____ BIS _____

AWARDS TODAY_____

POINTS COMING IN SHOW _____ POINTS EARNED TODAY _____ POINTS TO DATE _____

OTHER RESULTS/JUDGES (I.E. NOHS)_____

_____

NEW TITLE _____

COMMENTS AND TAKE-AWAYS

_____

_____

_____

_____

_____

SHOW PREPARATIONS AND FEES

SHOW ADDRESS/ETA _____

SHOW PHOTO TAKEN [YES] [NO] PHOTO SENT TO JUDGE [YES] [NO] PHOTOGRAPHER _____

FEES: ENTRY_____ PHOTOS_____ PARKING_____ GROOMING_____ HEALTH CLINICS_____

HANDLER NAME/FEE _____HEALTH CLINIC TIMES_____

HOTEL _____PET SITTER_____

THINGS TO REMEMBER _____

TODAY'S GOAL _____

POSITIVE AFFIRMATION _____

Dog Show Competition Log

SHOW DATE	NAME OF DOG/ARM BAND NUMBER	EVENT TYPE	NAME OF SHOW

CLASS ENTERED	PLACE IN CLASS	ENTRY IN CLASS	TOTAL ENTRY	POINTS	AWARD	GROUP	BEST IN SHOW

ENTRY BREAK DOWN_____RING #_____TIME_____BREEDS BEFORE_____

BREED JUDGE _____GROUP _____BIS _____

AWARDS TODAY_____

POINTS COMING IN SHOW _____ POINTS EARNED TODAY _____ POINTS TO DATE _____

OTHER RESULTS/JUDGES (I.E. NOHS)_____

_____

NEW TITLE _____

COMMENTS AND TAKE-AWAYS

_____

_____

_____

_____

_____

SHOW PREPARATIONS AND FEES

SHOW ADDRESS/ETA _____

SHOW PHOTO TAKEN [YES] [NO] PHOTO SENT TO JUDGE [YES] [NO] PHOTOGRAPHER_____

FEES: ENTRY_____ PHOTOS_____ PARKING_____ GROOMING_____ HEALTH CLINICS_____

HANDLER NAME/FEE _____HEALTH CLINIC TIMES_____

HOTEL _____PET SITTER_____

THINGS TO REMEMBER _____

TODAY'S GOAL _____

POSITIVE AFFIRMATION _____

Dog Show Competition Log

SHOW DATE	NAME OF DOG/ARM BAND NUMBER	EVENT TYPE	NAME OF SHOW

CLASS ENTERED	PLACE IN CLASS	ENTRY IN CLASS	TOTAL ENTRY	POINTS	AWARD	GROUP	BEST IN SHOW

ENTRY BREAK DOWN_____RING #_____TIME_____BREEDS BEFORE_____

BREED JUDGE _____GROUP _____ BIS _____

AWARDS TODAY_____

POINTS COMING IN SHOW _____ POINTS EARNED TODAY _____ POINTS TO DATE _____

OTHER RESULTS/JUDGES (I.E. NOHS)_____

_____

NEW TITLE _____

COMMENTS AND TAKE-AWAYS

_____

_____

_____

_____

_____

SHOW PREPARATIONS AND FEES

SHOW ADDRESS/ETA _____

SHOW PHOTO TAKEN [YES] [NO] PHOTO SENT TO JUDGE [YES] [NO] PHOTOGRAPHER _____

FEES: ENTRY_____ PHOTOS_____ PARKING_____ GROOMING_____ HEALTH CLINICS_____

HANDLER NAME/FEE _____HEALTH CLINIC TIMES_____

HOTEL _____PET SITTER_____

THINGS TO REMEMBER _____

TODAY'S GOAL _____

POSITIVE AFFIRMATION _____

Dog Show Competition Log

SHOW DATE	NAME OF DOG/ARM BAND NUMBER	EVENT TYPE	NAME OF SHOW

CLASS ENTERED	PLACE IN CLASS	ENTRY IN CLASS	TOTAL ENTRY	POINTS	AWARD	GROUP	BEST IN SHOW

ENTRY BREAK DOWN_____RING #_____TIME_____BREEDS BEFORE_____

BREED JUDGE _____GROUP _____BIS _____

AWARDS TODAY_____

POINTS COMING IN SHOW _____ POINTS EARNED TODAY _____ POINTS TO DATE _____

OTHER RESULTS/JUDGES (I.E. NOHS)_____

_____

NEW TITLE _____

COMMENTS AND TAKE-AWAYS

_____

_____

_____

_____

_____

SHOW PREPARATIONS AND FEES

SHOW ADDRESS/ETA _____

SHOW PHOTO TAKEN [YES] [NO] PHOTO SENT TO JUDGE [YES] [NO] PHOTOGRAPHER _____

FEES: ENTRY_____ PHOTOS_____ PARKING_____ GROOMING_____ HEALTH CLINICS_____

HANDLER NAME/FEE _____HEALTH CLINIC TIMES_____

HOTEL _____PET SITTER_____

THINGS TO REMEMBER _____

TODAY'S GOAL _____

POSITIVE AFFIRMATION _____

Dog Show Competition Log

SHOW DATE	NAME OF DOG/ARM BAND NUMBER	EVENT TYPE	NAME OF SHOW

CLASS ENTERED	PLACE IN CLASS	ENTRY IN CLASS	TOTAL ENTRY	POINTS	AWARD	GROUP	BEST IN SHOW

ENTRY BREAK DOWN_____RING #_____TIME_____BREEDS BEFORE_____

BREED JUDGE _____GROUP _____BIS _____

AWARDS TODAY_____

POINTS COMING IN SHOW _____ POINTS EARNED TODAY _____ POINTS TO DATE _____

OTHER RESULTS/JUDGES (I.E. NOHS)_____

_____

NEW TITLE _____

COMMENTS AND TAKE-AWAYS

_____

_____

_____

_____

_____

SHOW PREPARATIONS AND FEES

SHOW ADDRESS/ETA _____

SHOW PHOTO TAKEN ☐ YES ☐ NO PHOTO SENT TO JUDGE ☐ YES ☐ NO PHOTOGRAPHER _____

FEES: ENTRY_____ PHOTOS_____ PARKING_____ GROOMING_____ HEALTH CLINICS_____

HANDLER NAME/FEE _____HEALTH CLINIC TIMES_____

HOTEL _____PET SITTER_____

THINGS TO REMEMBER _____

TODAY'S GOAL _____

POSITIVE AFFIRMATION _____

Dog Show Competition Log

SHOW DATE	NAME OF DOG/ARM BAND NUMBER	EVENT TYPE	NAME OF SHOW

CLASS ENTERED	PLACE IN CLASS	ENTRY IN CLASS	TOTAL ENTRY	POINTS	AWARD	GROUP	BEST IN SHOW

ENTRY BREAK DOWN_____RING #_____TIME_____BREEDS BEFORE_____

BREED JUDGE _____GROUP _____BIS _____

AWARDS TODAY_____

POINTS COMING IN SHOW _____ POINTS EARNED TODAY _____ POINTS TO DATE _____

OTHER RESULTS/JUDGES (I.E. NOHS)_____

_____

NEW TITLE _____

COMMENTS AND TAKE-AWAYS

_____

_____

_____

_____

_____

SHOW PREPARATIONS AND FEES

SHOW ADDRESS/ETA _____

SHOW PHOTO TAKEN [YES] [NO] PHOTO SENT TO JUDGE [YES] [NO] PHOTOGRAPHER_____

FEES: ENTRY_____ PHOTOS_____ PARKING_____ GROOMING_____ HEALTH CLINICS_____

HANDLER NAME/FEE _____HEALTH CLINIC TIMES_____

HOTEL _____PET SITTER_____

THINGS TO REMEMBER _____

TODAY'S GOAL _____

POSITIVE AFFIRMATION _____

Dog Show Competition Log

SHOW DATE	NAME OF DOG/ARM BAND NUMBER	EVENT TYPE	NAME OF SHOW

CLASS ENTERED	PLACE IN CLASS	ENTRY IN CLASS	TOTAL ENTRY	POINTS	AWARD	GROUP	BEST IN SHOW

ENTRY BREAK DOWN_____RING #_____TIME_____BREEDS BEFORE_____

BREED JUDGE _____GROUP _____ BIS _____

AWARDS TODAY_____

POINTS COMING IN SHOW _____ POINTS EARNED TODAY _____ POINTS TO DATE _____

OTHER RESULTS/JUDGES (I.E. NOHS)_____

_____

NEW TITLE _____

COMMENTS AND TAKE-AWAYS

_____

_____

_____

_____

_____

SHOW PREPARATIONS AND FEES

SHOW ADDRESS/ETA _____

SHOW PHOTO TAKEN ☐ YES ☐ NO PHOTO SENT TO JUDGE ☐ YES ☐ NO PHOTOGRAPHER _____

FEES: ENTRY_____ PHOTOS_____ PARKING_____ GROOMING_____ HEALTH CLINICS_____

HANDLER NAME/FEE _____HEALTH CLINIC TIMES_____

HOTEL _____PET SITTER_____

THINGS TO REMEMBER _____

TODAY'S GOAL _____

POSITIVE AFFIRMATION _____

Dog Show Competition Log

SHOW DATE	NAME OF DOG/ARM BAND NUMBER	EVENT TYPE	NAME OF SHOW

CLASS ENTERED	PLACE IN CLASS	ENTRY IN CLASS	TOTAL ENTRY	POINTS	AWARD	GROUP	BEST IN SHOW

ENTRY BREAK DOWN_____RING #_____TIME_____BREEDS BEFORE_____

BREED JUDGE _____GROUP _____BIS _____

AWARDS TODAY_____

POINTS COMING IN SHOW _____ POINTS EARNED TODAY _____ POINTS TO DATE _____

OTHER RESULTS/JUDGES (I.E. NOHS)_____

_____

NEW TITLE _____

COMMENTS AND TAKE-AWAYS

_____

_____

_____

_____

_____

SHOW PREPARATIONS AND FEES

SHOW ADDRESS/ETA _____

SHOW PHOTO TAKEN [YES] [NO] PHOTO SENT TO JUDGE [YES] [NO] PHOTOGRAPHER _____

FEES: ENTRY_____ PHOTOS_____ PARKING_____ GROOMING_____ HEALTH CLINICS_____

HANDLER NAME/FEE _____HEALTH CLINIC TIMES_____

HOTEL _____PET SITTER_____

THINGS TO REMEMBER _____

TODAY'S GOAL _____

POSITIVE AFFIRMATION _____

Dog Show Competition Log

SHOW DATE	NAME OF DOG/ARM BAND NUMBER	EVENT TYPE	NAME OF SHOW

CLASS ENTERED	PLACE IN CLASS	ENTRY IN CLASS	TOTAL ENTRY	POINTS	AWARD	GROUP	BEST IN SHOW

ENTRY BREAK DOWN_____ RING #_____ TIME_____ BREEDS BEFORE_____

BREED JUDGE _____ GROUP _____ BIS _____

AWARDS TODAY_____

POINTS COMING IN SHOW _____ POINTS EARNED TODAY _____ POINTS TO DATE _____

OTHER RESULTS/JUDGES (I.E. NOHS)_____

_____

NEW TITLE _____

COMMENTS AND TAKE-AWAYS

_____

_____

_____

_____

_____

SHOW PREPARATIONS AND FEES

SHOW ADDRESS/ETA _____

SHOW PHOTO TAKEN [YES] [NO] PHOTO SENT TO JUDGE [YES] [NO] PHOTOGRAPHER_____

FEES: ENTRY_____ PHOTOS_____ PARKING_____ GROOMING_____ HEALTH CLINICS_____

HANDLER NAME/FEE _____ HEALTH CLINIC TIMES_____

HOTEL _____ PET SITTER_____

THINGS TO REMEMBER _____

TODAY'S GOAL _____

POSITIVE AFFIRMATION _____

Dog Show Competition Log

SHOW DATE	NAME OF DOG/ARM BAND NUMBER	EVENT TYPE	NAME OF SHOW

CLASS ENTERED	PLACE IN CLASS	ENTRY IN CLASS	TOTAL ENTRY	POINTS	AWARD	GROUP	BEST IN SHOW

ENTRY BREAK DOWN_____RING #_____TIME_____BREEDS BEFORE_____

BREED JUDGE _____GROUP _____ BIS _____

AWARDS TODAY_____

POINTS COMING IN SHOW _____ POINTS EARNED TODAY _____ POINTS TO DATE _____

OTHER RESULTS/JUDGES (I.E. NOHS)_____

_____

NEW TITLE _____

COMMENTS AND TAKE-AWAYS

_____

_____

_____

_____

_____

SHOW PREPARATIONS AND FEES

SHOW ADDRESS/ETA _____

SHOW PHOTO TAKEN [YES] [NO] PHOTO SENT TO JUDGE [YES] [NO] PHOTOGRAPHER_____

FEES: ENTRY_____ PHOTOS_____ PARKING_____ GROOMING_____ HEALTH CLINICS_____

HANDLER NAME/FEE _____HEALTH CLINIC TIMES_____

HOTEL _____PET SITTER_____

THINGS TO REMEMBER _____

TODAY'S GOAL _____

POSITIVE AFFIRMATION _____

Dog Show Competition Log

SHOW DATE	NAME OF DOG/ARM BAND NUMBER	EVENT TYPE	NAME OF SHOW

CLASS ENTERED	PLACE IN CLASS	ENTRY IN CLASS	TOTAL ENTRY	POINTS	AWARD	GROUP	BEST IN SHOW

ENTRY BREAK DOWN_____RING #_____TIME_____BREEDS BEFORE_____

BREED JUDGE _____GROUP _____ BIS _____

AWARDS TODAY_____

POINTS COMING IN SHOW _____ POINTS EARNED TODAY _____ POINTS TO DATE _____

OTHER RESULTS/JUDGES (I.E. NOHS)_____

_____

NEW TITLE _____

COMMENTS AND TAKE-AWAYS

_____

_____

_____

_____

_____

SHOW PREPARATIONS AND FEES

SHOW ADDRESS/ETA _____

SHOW PHOTO TAKEN ☐ YES ☐ NO PHOTO SENT TO JUDGE ☐ YES ☐ NO PHOTOGRAPHER_____

FEES: ENTRY_____ PHOTOS_____ PARKING_____ GROOMING_____ HEALTH CLINICS_____

HANDLER NAME/FEE _____HEALTH CLINIC TIMES_____

HOTEL _____PET SITTER_____

THINGS TO REMEMBER _____

TODAY'S GOAL _____

POSITIVE AFFIRMATION _____

Dog Show Competition Log

SHOW DATE	NAME OF DOG/ARM BAND NUMBER	EVENT TYPE	NAME OF SHOW

CLASS ENTERED	PLACE IN CLASS	ENTRY IN CLASS	TOTAL ENTRY	POINTS	AWARD	GROUP	BEST IN SHOW

ENTRY BREAK DOWN_____RING #_____TIME_____BREEDS BEFORE_____

BREED JUDGE _____GROUP _____BIS _____

AWARDS TODAY_____

POINTS COMING IN SHOW _____ POINTS EARNED TODAY _____ POINTS TO DATE _____

OTHER RESULTS/JUDGES (I.E. NOHS)_____

_____

NEW TITLE _____

COMMENTS AND TAKE-AWAYS

_____

_____

_____

_____

_____

SHOW PREPARATIONS AND FEES

SHOW ADDRESS/ETA _____

SHOW PHOTO TAKEN [YES] [NO] PHOTO SENT TO JUDGE [YES] [NO] PHOTOGRAPHER _____

FEES: ENTRY_____ PHOTOS_____ PARKING_____ GROOMING_____ HEALTH CLINICS_____

HANDLER NAME/FEE _____HEALTH CLINIC TIMES_____

HOTEL _____PET SITTER_____

THINGS TO REMEMBER _____

TODAY'S GOAL _____

POSITIVE AFFIRMATION _____

Dog Show Competition Log

SHOW DATE	NAME OF DOG/ARM BAND NUMBER	EVENT TYPE	NAME OF SHOW

CLASS ENTERED	PLACE IN CLASS	ENTRY IN CLASS	TOTAL ENTRY	POINTS	AWARD	GROUP	BEST IN SHOW

ENTRY BREAK DOWN_____RING #_____TIME_____BREEDS BEFORE_____

BREED JUDGE _____GROUP _____ BIS _____

AWARDS TODAY_____

POINTS COMING IN SHOW _____ POINTS EARNED TODAY _____ POINTS TO DATE _____

OTHER RESULTS/JUDGES (I.E. NOHS)_____

_____

NEW TITLE _____

COMMENTS AND TAKE-AWAYS

_____

_____

_____

_____

_____

SHOW PREPARATIONS AND FEES

SHOW ADDRESS/ETA _____

SHOW PHOTO TAKEN [YES] [NO] PHOTO SENT TO JUDGE [YES] [NO] PHOTOGRAPHER_____

FEES: ENTRY_____ PHOTOS_____ PARKING_____ GROOMING_____ HEALTH CLINICS_____

HANDLER NAME/FEE _____HEALTH CLINIC TIMES_____

HOTEL _____PET SITTER_____

THINGS TO REMEMBER _____

TODAY'S GOAL _____

POSITIVE AFFIRMATION _____

Dog Show Competition Log

SHOW DATE	NAME OF DOG/ARM BAND NUMBER	EVENT TYPE	NAME OF SHOW

CLASS ENTERED	PLACE IN CLASS	ENTRY IN CLASS	TOTAL ENTRY	POINTS	AWARD	GROUP	BEST IN SHOW

ENTRY BREAK DOWN_____RING #_____TIME_____BREEDS BEFORE_____

BREED JUDGE _____GROUP _____ BIS _____

AWARDS TODAY_____

POINTS COMING IN SHOW _____ POINTS EARNED TODAY _____ POINTS TO DATE _____

OTHER RESULTS/JUDGES (I.E. NOHS)_____

_____

NEW TITLE _____

COMMENTS AND TAKE-AWAYS

_____

_____

_____

_____

_____

SHOW PREPARATIONS AND FEES

SHOW ADDRESS/ETA _____

SHOW PHOTO TAKEN [YES] [NO] PHOTO SENT TO JUDGE [YES] [NO] PHOTOGRAPHER_____

FEES: ENTRY_____ PHOTOS_____ PARKING_____ GROOMING_____ HEALTH CLINICS_____

HANDLER NAME/FEE _____HEALTH CLINIC TIMES_____

HOTEL _____PET SITTER_____

THINGS TO REMEMBER _____

TODAY'S GOAL _____

POSITIVE AFFIRMATION _____

Dog Show Competition Log

SHOW DATE	NAME OF DOG/ARM BAND NUMBER	EVENT TYPE	NAME OF SHOW

CLASS ENTERED	PLACE IN CLASS	ENTRY IN CLASS	TOTAL ENTRY	POINTS	AWARD	GROUP	BEST IN SHOW

ENTRY BREAK DOWN_____RING #_____TIME_____BREEDS BEFORE_____

BREED JUDGE _____GROUP _____BIS _____

AWARDS TODAY_____

POINTS COMING IN SHOW _____ POINTS EARNED TODAY _____ POINTS TO DATE _____

OTHER RESULTS/JUDGES (I.E. NOHS)_____

_____

NEW TITLE _____

COMMENTS AND TAKE-AWAYS

_____

_____

_____

_____

_____

SHOW PREPARATIONS AND FEES

SHOW ADDRESS/ETA _____

SHOW PHOTO TAKEN ☐ YES ☐ NO PHOTO SENT TO JUDGE ☐ YES ☐ NO PHOTOGRAPHER_____

FEES: ENTRY_____ PHOTOS_____ PARKING_____ GROOMING_____ HEALTH CLINICS_____

HANDLER NAME/FEE _____HEALTH CLINIC TIMES_____

HOTEL _____PET SITTER_____

THINGS TO REMEMBER _____

TODAY'S GOAL _____

POSITIVE AFFIRMATION _____

Notes

Part 3
Show Talk & Tips

My little dog— a
heartbeat at my feet.

—Edith Wharton

❖ ❖❖ ❖ Brief History of Dog Shows ❖ ❖❖ ❖

The history of dogs matters because it helps us celebrate the human-canine bond and lays a solid foundation for all we do as dog fanciers. Have you ever wondered when, where, and how dog shows began? Dennis Homes, breed historian from the UK Cavalier Club, shares his insight in this article.

There is no single animal species on Earth as diverse in both size and appearance as a dog. From the tiny Chihuahua to the Neapolitan Mastiff or the Chinese Crested to the Great Dane, they differ so greatly and yet they are all the same species. Nobody knows for sure how the human-canine bond first came about, and for many years, experts believed domestication first occurred around twelve thousand years ago. However, recent archaeological digs in places as far apart as Belgium and Eastern Russia have discovered fossilized remains of domestic dogs in early human encampments that date back to around twenty-five thousand years ago. How canine domestication came about is the subject of much speculation, but it does appear that dogs evolved from a wolf-type ancestor.

Dogs were probably first used by humans for work functions such as guarding, herding, retrieving, catching vermin, etc. Those that excelled at certain functions were most likely bred with others that had a similar trait and over time this is how certain breed types evolved. It wasn't until around five hundred years ago that dogs were bred purely for their looks, and these were probably only among companion pets of ladies from wealthy or aristocratic families. By and large, most dogs were bred for their working abilities.

Showing dogs, otherwise known as the "sport of conformation," did not start until around the mid-1800s. The earliest known record of a dog show was in 1859 in Newcastle-upon-Tyne in England, where Pointers and Setters were exhibited. There soon followed many other small shows where breeders could exhibit their dogs and display to other enthusiasts what type of dogs their kennels were producing. Although breeders were competing against each other, the primary motive of these early dog shows was to display their dogs to the public at large.

There was no registration system or keeping of pedigrees at this time, so as these shows started to become more popular the English Kennel Club was set up in 1873 to provide rules and regulations for dog shows and to provide an accurate register of pedigrees. Dog shows were also starting to gain popularity in the United States, and in 1884 the American Kennel Club (AKC) was established to maintain breeding records of purebred dogs in the United States. In 1911 the Federation Cynologique Internationle (FCI) was established; it is based in Belgium and oversees the rules of national kennel clubs from around 75 different countries.

Throughout the twentieth century dog shows gained huge popularity all over the world and to many people it is regarded as a sport. Obviously sport is closely linked with competitiveness, which in turn leads to rivalry. The terms "sportsmanship" and "sportsmanlike" are linked to the word "fairness" as epitomized in the true spirit of the Olympic Games. Competitiveness, in this sense, encourages people to strive to improve their personal best, respect their opponent, and graciously accept a win or a loss. However, the downside of competitiveness is where rivalry leads to jealousy. If dog showing is to be likened to a sport, then it is imperative that there should be friendly rivalry and fairness, as at the end of the day, we are dealing with living animals, and the welfare of these animals should always be our number one priority. Showing dogs should be about exhibitors and breeders striving to improve their dogs in breed type, appearance and soundness. It is also important to ensure they are healthy and still have the physical function they were originally bred for, even though we do not necessarily use them for that purpose.

Dennis Homes is an author, judge, and dog breeder at Leogem Cavalier UK.

❖ ❖ ❖ ❖ About Conformation Shows ❖ ❖ ❖ ❖

There's so much that goes into the making of a show dog, as well as the organization of a show. It takes a village! Having experienced life on stage, I can't help but see similarities between the journey a dancer takes to achieve her dreams and the efforts to produce a memorable dog show. There's hard work, maybe even tears. But in the end, when the curtain rises, and the music plays, excitement and a sense of achievement are in the air. Let's peek behind the scenes to gain insight into what the show is about.

THE PURPOSE OF THE SHOW

At first glance, a dog show may seem like a beauty pageant. But it's not. The purpose of a conformation show is to evaluate breeding stock. It's not about which dog is the prettiest, but which dog comes closest (conforms) to its breed standard— the perfect picture of how a dog should look, move and behave, with their function in mind. Why is this important? Because the closer a dog's appearance is to the standard, the better that dog's ability to produce quality purebred puppies. Intertwined in this purpose is that conformation shows help educate spectators about the ideal qualities and function of a particular breed, which in turn helps hopeful pet parents choose just the right furry friend for their lifestyle and home.

There are three types of AKC Conformation Shows:

- *All-Breed Shows:* Competitions offered to over 175 breeds and varieties of AKC recognized dogs.

- *Specialty Shows:* Restricted to dogs of a certain breed or varieties of one breed.

- *Group Shows:* Limited to dogs belonging to one of the seven groups (i.e., Sporting, Hound, Toy).

What about non-registered pure and mixed breeds? Can they compete too?

Since conformation shows are specifically designed to evaluate breeding stock, with the goal to protect and enhance certain breeds of purebred dogs, mixed breeds and spayed or neutered purebreds are ineligible to compete. However, owners of these beloved dogs have opportunities to "show off" their dogs through other programs created with them in mind. *See resource page 186 for more information.*

The purpose of a conformation dog show— to evaluate breeding stock.

THE PERFORMERS—IT TAKES A VILLAGE!

THE STAR OF THE SHOW

The star of the show, of course, is your dog. All other roles work together to help him stay tail-wagging happy, shiny, and show-ready! Is a star born or made? Both. The making of a show dog begins way before he is born, with breeders carefully selecting sire and dam to better their lines. If all goes well and a pup is born that conforms closely to its breed standard, the long journey to get him show-ready begins. With that in mind, there's obviously a lot that will go into the making of your show dog. But to start, it's good to know why your precious prodigy was bred. What was his original function? These are the seven groups featured at All-Breed AKC shows. Dogs are grouped by their function . . .

The seven groups featured at All-Breed shows:

Sporting: Bred to hunt game birds both on land and in the water: i.e., Pointers, Retrievers, Setters, Spaniels.

Hound: Bred for hunting other game by sight or scent: i.e., Beagles, Bassets, Dachshunds and Greyhounds.

Working: Bred to pull carts, guard property, and perform search and rescue services. Among the breeds in this group are the Akita, Boxer, Doberman Pinscher, and St. Bernard.

Terrier: Bred to rid property of vermin such as rats: i.e., Airedale, Cairn Terrier and Scottish Terrier.

Toy: Bred to be household companions: i.e., Cavalier King Charles Spaniel, Chihuahua, Pomeranian, Pug.

Non-Sporting: This diverse group includes the Chow Chow, Bulldog, Dalmatian and Poodle. These dogs vary in size and function, and many are considered companion dogs.

Herding: These dogs were bred to help shepherds and ranchers herd their livestock. The Briard, Collie, German Shepherd Dog and Old English Sheepdog are some of the breeds in this group.

THE LEADING ROLES

Exhibitor/Handler: This can be the dog's owner, breeder, or a hired professional. They represent the dog in the ring. From pre-show to show-day prep, they are responsible for almost everything related to his care. The handler is also the dog's partner. Imagine dancing the waltz. For the most part, you are the one leading your dog. But occasionally, when you're feeling discouraged or unsure, don't be surprised if your canine partner takes the lead. Dogs can sense our mood and know how to offer those much-needed puppy kisses to lift us and help us carry on.

Judge: Judges, who are experienced purebred dog experts, evaluate the dogs' physical characteristics, movement/gait, and temperament to determine which dog most closely resembles the ideal characteristics of their respective breed standard. Judges examine ("go over") each dog with their hands to see how well the teeth, muscles, bones, and coat texture conform to the breed's standard. They observe the dog's overall balance in profile and on the move. Finally, they hand out awards/ribbons according to how closely each dog compares to their mental image of the "perfect" dog in the breed's official standard.

SUPPORTING ROLES

Ring Steward: The person (usually a volunteer from the organizing club) who assists the judge in the ring, ensuring things run smoothly. Some of their duties include checking in exhibitors, calling classes, and getting ribbons ready to hand out.

Host Club: These individuals and clubs organize the show (plan the venue, select judges, set up/tear down the rings, etc.) and work to keep things running smoothly and everyone safe. They also typically run health clinics, which are essential to maintain each breed's health. Consider volunteering to help your club.

Superintendent: This is an official or management company licensed by a kennel club to manage a show.

Show Vendors: They provide valuable and fun dog show products to help you and your dog shine. And we can't forget the food stands and trucks which help keep our tummies from rumbling!

The Audience: We must remember the spectators! They support the exhibitors, the dogs, and the sport with their attendance, enthusiastic cheers, and applause—*more on interacting with the audience on page 156.*

Certainly, many contribute to the show's success behind the scenes, such as on-site vets, show photographers, and cleanup crews. It's always good to show appreciation and remember they are part of the "village."

THE STAGE—HOW THE STORY GOES . . .

A dog show is basically a choreographed event. Here's a brief synopsis of how the story goes . . .

When the curtains open, many handlers with their doggies are on stage. Each dog/handler team is competing for a prize. There will be several "Acts," each taking place along a road with lots of highs and lows.

At the end of the show, through a process of elimination, one dog will be left standing in the spotlight. This dog will be awarded BEST IN SHOW, and another lucky doggie will be named Reserve Best in Show!

Let's peek behind the scenes and take a stroll along the **Road to Best in Show** . . .

THE ROAD TO BEST IN SHOW

Visit www.akc.org to learn about other exciting competitions you may be eligible for with your dogs, such as AKC National Owner-Handled Series, Four-to-Six Month Beginner Puppy Competition, or Junior Showmanship.

1.

At the start of a conformation show, lots of dogs are competing. If it's an All-Breed show, dogs of all breeds, shapes, and sizes will be there. If it's a Specialty Show, it's only for dogs of a particular breed. At the end of the show, only one dog will remain standing, undefeated, and be awarded Best in Show!

And they're off . . .

2.

CLASS DOGS COMPETE: Each dog is presented to a judge by its handler—its owner, breeder, or a hired professional. Males and females compete separately in their respective breeds in seven Regular Classes: Puppy (6-9, and 9-12 Months), 12-18 Months, Novice, Amateur-Owner-Handler, Bred by Exhibitor, American-Bred, and Open.

THE CLASSES

Counting points along the way . . .

3.

Most dogs at conformation shows are competing for points towards their AKC championships. It takes 15 points, including two majors (wins of 3,4,5), awarded by at least three different judges, to become an AKC "Champion of Record." The number of points awarded depends on the number of males ("dogs") and females ("bitches") of the breed actually in competition. The maximum number of points awarded at a show is 5 points.

4.

After regular classes are judged, all the first-place dogs compete again to see who is the best of the winning dogs. Males and females are judged separately. Only the best male (Winners Dog) and the best female (Winners Bitch) receive championship points. *Reserve Winners* are then chosen for each sex.

Winner's Dog (WD) and Winner's Bitch (WB) move on to compete with the champions for the Best of Breed award!

WD   WB

WD and WB advance to the Best of Breed competition!

At the end of the Best of Breed Competition three awards are usually given:

5.

Best of Breed (BOB): Judged best in its breed. May be awarded Grand Champion points.

Best of Winners (BOW): Judged as the better of the Winners Dog and Winners Bitch.

Best of Opposite Sex (BOS): Best dog that is the opposite sex to the Best of Breed winner. If Champion of record, may receive Grand Champion points.

BEST OF BREED COMPETITION

BEST OF BREED (BOB)

6.

After BOB is chosen, Select awards are given. These are similar to Awards of Merit. Selects are the next best in competition. The Select Dog and Bitch are eligible for Grand Champion points.

Only the BOB winner advances to the Group competition to represent his breed . .

7.

GROUPS COMPETITION: Each AKC recognized breed falls into one of seven group classifications: Sporting, Hound, Working, Terrier, Toy, Non-Sporting and Herding. Four placements are awarded in each group, but only the first-place winner advances to the Best in Show competition.

GROUP COMPETITION

The seven 1st place Group winners advance to Best in Show competition!

BEST IN SHOW COMPETITION

8.

BEST IN SHOW COMPETITION: The fabulous seven group winners are brought into the ring, accompanied by cheers and applause, where they compete for BEST IN SHOW, the highest award at a dog show!

And finally . . .

BEST IN SHOW (BIS)

9.

After careful deliberation, the judge awards one dog Best in Show. This dog stands alone, remaining undefeated. Reserve Best in Show (RBIS) is selected from the remaining Group winners. Applause and excitement fill the air! Congratulations are offered. While photos are taken, the BIS dog stands in the spotlight, adorned by a gorgeous rosette.

THE SPOTLIGHT

The road to best in show is not the only time you and your dog will be in the spotlight. All along the way, folks will be watching you prep your dog for the ring (i.e., groom, walk, train). They may also want to pet your dog and ask questions. That's not a bad thing, but while competing, it's not always easy. Here are some tips to help you handle the spotlight with grace.

- **Embrace your role as a canine ambassador:** As dedicated dog fanciers and exhibitors, we serve as the official representatives of one of the most amazing and intelligent creatures on earth. This responsibility extends beyond the show ring. We are their voice—showcasing their incredible attributes and advocating for their well-being. We also represent and uphold the future of canine sports. When possible, embrace the opportunity to share your passion for the sport and the dogs you love. Learn about AKC's Canine Ambassador program at www.akc.org/public-education/canine-ambassador-program/

- **Remember people are watching:** Sometimes we get so caught up in the "show" we forget people are watching. Whether grooming our dogs ringside, training them, or interacting with fellow competitors, we can lead by example. It's the best publicity for the dogs and sport we love.

- **Be open to sharing your knowledge:** At shows, you may encounter curious spectators with questions. Create a welcoming atmosphere and, when feasible, offer insights about purebred dogs, grooming, training, and more. Occasionally, folks attend shows to explore dog breeds and seek guidance in finding responsible breeders. Embrace the opportunity to direct them toward informed choices.

- **If you're too busy to talk:** Many attendees lack awareness of proper etiquette when approaching exhibitors at a canine sports event. If you're busy preparing for your event and someone wants to talk about your dogs, kindly ask them to wait until you're done. Inform them of your availability, if and when.

- **When people want to pet your pooch:** Politely remind people to "ask" before petting your dog or giving a treat. Mention that some dogs have special dietary needs or have sensitive stomachs. It's also an opportune moment to instruct a child on the proper way to approach a dog. The ask-before-petting rule also applies to touching a dog through a crate or while in a pen. If this happens, clarify that it's your dog's private space and time to rest. You could also explain that even friendly dogs might nip if approached in certain ways or situations.

- **When people are eager to learn more:** There are many wonderful topics to share about dogs and canine sports, and we may not necessarily have all the answers or time to share. For those eager to learn, direct them to the AKC website. The American Kennel Club's Public Education department provides various resources designed to educate individuals of all ages about the wonderful world of dogs. Visit www.akc.org/public-education/resources/

Photo: Our daughter as a youngster happily showing a spectator how we brush our Cavalier King Charles Spaniel show dogs. What a good little canine ambassador!

Training for the Show

No show dog is made overnight. Getting him shiny, well-trained, and show-ready can take months, a year, or more. With that in mind, a lot will go into the making of your show dog and your success in the ring. Ultimately, what wins in the ring is a great dog partnered with a great handler. These dog show tips are not exhaustive but will certainly help you put your best paw forward while dancing around the ring with your partner pooch and reaching for those colorful ribbons!

PRE-SHOW TIPS

KNOW YOUR BREED STANDARD

The standard describes the characteristics (structure, temperament, and movement) that allow each breed to perform the function for which it was bred, such as herding and retrieving. With that in mind, you'll want to memorize the standard of the breed you are showing and know how your dog measures up, meaning his strengths and weaknesses. This information will help you minimize his faults and accentuate his virtues to create an ideal presentation for the judge in the ring. The official written standard for each breed is maintained by the breed's national club and included in *The Complete Dog Book* published by the AKC.

SOCIALIZE REGULARLY

Even with super conformation, a pup with stage fright or people fright will be hard to show. Once your pup is appropriately vaccinated, take him with you everywhere. The socialization process involves exposing your pup to new people, places, situations, sounds, etc. Here are some tips to get the process going:

- Enroll in puppy kindergarten. It's a great way to expose your pup to new people, other pups, and noises.

- Walk your pup on various surfaces (i.e., grass, cement, carpet, rubber matting) to get his precious paws ready for various show venues and the ring mats.

- When you're out and about, encourage people to gently and properly pet your pup so he gets used to being touched by strangers—he will meet many judges at shows. All these experiences will help your pup enter the ring with confidence. And everyone loves a confident "showy" dog in the ring!

JOIN A HANDLING CLASS

The two essentials a show dog needs to learn are how to stand (stack) and walk (gait) for the ring. The best place to learn these is in a handling class. These classes recreate a show setting, preparing you and your dog for the spotlight. **Things you may practice:** "stacking your dog," both on the table and the ground, a "free stack," gaiting them gracefully at your side, and basic movement patterns like the "down and back" (up and back), "triangle," and "L" pattern. These classes also help your dog get accustomed to a judge's examination, exposure to new sounds, and interaction with new people and fellow pups. You'll also gain tips on "baiting your dog." Try various treats to discover your dog's favorites. Training your dog to respond to food, toys, or a clicker is essential—just be sure not to distract other dogs or exhibitors with noises.

There's lots more to learn! The best part is all these experiences will acquaint you and your dog with the dynamics of a dog show, offering valuable insights into what's ahead. To find a handling class, connect with your local dog club. Begin your pup's training early and keep things fun.

Other avenues for learning include (1) Handling seminars, found through your local kennel club or the AKC Events Calendar online. (2) Conformation Video tutorials on YouTube, often led by professional handlers. (3) Books available on Amazon under "Dog Show Training Books." Reading reviews can help you choose. (4) The AKC Match Program at www.akc.org. A match is a great place to practice in a relaxed, fun setting.

FIND A DOG SHOW MENTOR

Benefits of a mentor: The mentor-mentee relationship can be incredibly rewarding to your dog show journey. Think of the mentor as a coach, offering guidance while cheering you on. Of course, you could go the journey alone, as many do, but how wonderful to be accompanied by a kind mentor to help you learn and grow while avoiding the potential pitfalls. With time, you'll gain your wings and lean less and less on your mentor, which is normal. But they'll likely always be there for you.

To find a mentor: Your all-breed kennel club is an excellent place to find a mentor. You can network with breeders, make friends, and look for potential mentors you might be compatible with.

If you don't have a mentor, take heart; you can still succeed. You can find honest critiques and guidance at handling classes, through online programs, seminars, and support groups. For more ideas, subscribe to dog show magazines like *Showsight* and the *AKC Events Calendar* (see page 186). Also, reach out to the pros with questions. At one of my first shows, I asked a professional handler in my breed what grooming tools she recommended. She graciously opened her tack box and offered advice. At that moment, she was mentoring, leading by example. As you gain expertise, there will be numerous opportunities to give back.

KEEP UP WITH GROOMING

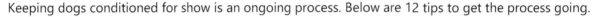

Keeping dogs conditioned for show is an ongoing process. Below are 12 tips to get the process going.

1. **Invest in grooming equipment:** Having the right tools will make grooming easier. These essentials will get you started: Invest in a sturdy **Grooming Table,** complete with a grooming arm, short lead, and slip collar to ensure your dog's safety and stability. Introduce your dog to the table early on. For show travels, consider these options: (1) Crate tops with non-slip surface. (2) Folding grooming table on wheels, doubles as a dolly to transport equipment. *Remember, never leave your dog unattended on the table.* **A Tack Box** is also essential. This is a container to store smaller grooming items like brushes, combs, sprays, and scissors. You can purchase one or repurpose an existing bag or box. Refer to page 182 for common grooming items. *Keep equipment clean. Discard and replace damaged items, i.e. combs with bent pins.*

2. **Keep the standard in mind:** The breed standard shows us what to aim for when grooming for show. For example, for a Cavalier King Charles Spaniel, the AKC standard for the coat specifies, "Of moderate length, silky, free from curl. Slight wave permissible. Feathering on ears, chest, legs and tail should be long, and the feathering on the feet is a feature of the breed. No trimming of the dog is permitted."Familiarize yourself with what is required for your dog breed and groom accordingly.

3. **Breed-specific grooming:** Some breeds are "wash and wear," others require more extensive grooming, like the Poodle. Reach out to other exhibitors in your breed for guidance, search on YouTube for show grooming tutorials, or attend grooming seminars. Many national and local breed clubs have grooming seminars and resources. You can also find a competent show groomer and ask if you can pay for a lesson.

4. **Exercise your dog:** A fit dog has a unique beauty. Engage your show dog in regular physical activity. Many show dogs do roadwork, meaning they run alongside a bike or on a dog trotter. Learn what type of exercise is appropriate for your breed. Keep it fun for your pooch.

5. **Feed high-quality dog food:** If your dog experiences skin, coat, or tear staining issues, it might be linked to food allergies. Research foods and consult your vet to identify the ideal diet tailored to your dog's needs.. The journey to finding the perfect food might require some patience.

6. **Brush daily:** A daily brushing helps a dog's coat stay smooth, shiny, and knot-free. It's no fun dealing with mats or a dull coat the day before the show. It also allows you to check their bottom and ensure it's clean with no dried poop or anal gland issues. A daily "brushing out" also gets your dog used to being handled. Keep these sessions calm and soothing, using a gentle voice. End with treats and praise.

7. **Don't slack on the teeth:** Neglecting your dog's teeth not only leads to dental issues but also detracts from a polished presentation. Imagine the judge opening your dog's mouth and being welcomed by dirty teeth, bad breath, or a dog that bolts back. Begin with your pup early, building positive associations with mouth touching. Gradually work to lift his lip for gum massage and teeth cleaning. Use a finger brush or a soft rubber-bristle toothbrush with doggie toothpaste. Brush daily to eliminate plaque and debris. Consult your vet about dental cleanings.

8. **Don't forget the nails and foot fur:** Some breeds have lots of foot fur, so people tend to forget to trim the nails. Nails should be checked regularly. Also, remember the *dewclaw*, comparable to our thumb or big toe. Because they don't make ground contact, they can curl in and pierce the flesh. Overgrown nails lead to discomfort and hinder a dog's movement. Keep the foot fur (the hair between the pads and underside) clean and neatly trimmed. This helps with traction when dogs move on different surfaces.

9. **Don't forget the eyes and ears:** Dirty ears can become infected and painful. Use a vet-recommended gentle ear cleaner. Check your dogs' ears regularly, especially if they have floppy/long ears. Keep ear tips clean and dry. The eyes should also be free of discharge. Other than not being aesthetic, goopy eyes can be a sign of illness. Contact your vet with any concerns about your dog's health.

10. **Keep your dog clean:** It goes without saying judges like to touch a clean dog. Bathing, like all grooming, involves both maintenance and show-day care. Long before the show, research how often it is appropriate to bathe your dog. Some dogs with white coats may need a weekly bath to avoid staining. Even if your dog doesn't need to wash this often, you can still spot-bathe areas like the face, foot fur, and undercarriage. Try several shampoos and conditioners until you find the best brand for your dog's skin and fur. **As a general rule for coat maintenance, keep the coat clean and dry.**

    Show day prep: Apart from routine maintenance baths, most breeds are bathed the day before the show weekend, followed by brushing and spot-bathing on the show day. Practice and learn what's best for your dog. If suitable, use a deep conditioner on your dog the day before or day of the show. This can help the coat look sleek and shiny. Rinse out all the product so it doesn't leave a heavy residue and dull the coat.

11. **Practice Practice:** Practice makes perfect! That goes for our handling as well as grooming skills. If you aren't sure about the best way to groom your dog for show or found those tried and true products, keep asking questions, observing seasoned exhibitors, attending seminars, and learning. Stop by the vendors, too, and get advice on grooming products. Then practice at home on your dog. It can take months to years to hone grooming skills. Be patient. Have fun primping your pup for show! *Refer to page 185 for a sample grooming calendar. Using a calendar will help you set and keep grooming goals.*

12. **Stay relaxed on show day:** While our dogs must dazzle the judge, remember not to obsess over every strand of fur while waiting ringside. Constantly fiddling with your dog's eyes, ears, paws, and coat might inadvertently stress them out. If you've prepared well, just a few swift touch-ups suffice before entering the ring. However, remember that accidents can happen like your dog getting loose stool or drooling and messing up his feathering before entering the ring. It's happened to all of us. Stay calm. Use baby wipes, paper towels, or whatever's at hand, and carry on. Handling challenges gracefully is all part of the journey to Best in Show.

WORK ON PRESENTATION

Sometimes we get so focused on how our dog looks in the ring that we overlook our own presentation. Remember, it's a partnership, like dancing the waltz. If one partner appears confident and the other is nervous or distracted, it detracts from the overall presentation. Typically, it's the handler hindering the presentation, not the dog. Ask yourself— Are my shoulders tense or relaxed in the ring? Am I gripping the lead or holding it gently? Does the rhythm of my steps and speed help or hinder the gait of my dog at a walk, trot, canter, or gallop? Where is my focus while in the ring? Basic body awareness and presentation are needed for the waltz to flow well. **Here are eight tips to help you:**

1. **Video yourself:** While holding the leash, evaluating our handling skills can be challenging. Have a friend video you while practicing with your dog. *Here are a few things to consider:*

   Assess your speed. Video your dog coming and going away (and going around) to evaluate his best speed so you can adjust your speed as needed. **Also, consider how you hold the lead.** Holding a lead tightly can affect a dog's movement, creating artificial faults. Using a loose lead is best for a dog to be in balance. **Assess the dog's silhouette (and yours) while stacking.** Using a standing mirror helps. Practice *hand stacking* and a *free stack*. As you video yourself over time, you'll discover what to focus on.

2. **Watch the pros:** Stand ringside and watch the top handlers. What can you learn from the way they handle a dog? Use your Smartphone or IPad to get a quick video to study later.

3. **Breathe:** Nerves can get the best of us. Our dogs feel it, too, through our hands and the show lead. Take slow, deep breaths before entering the ring. Calm your mind. Relax your shoulders. Be in the moment. Dogs pick up on the calm, which helps them too.

4. **Stay fit:** Whether gaiting your dog in the ring or kneeling to stack him, basic fitness can improve the overall presentation and reduce the risk of injury (i.e., knee issues). Ask your doctor about a fitness plan. Also, check out AKC's FIT DOG program. It can bring health benefits to both you and your dog.

5. **Consider your wardrobe:** Clothing is like the backdrop on a stage. Imagine how difficult it would be to see dancers wearing dark costumes on a stage with a black backdrop. Similarly, what we wear can help or hinder the overall presentation. Choose clothes that compliment your dog and help the judge accurately see movement—more on page 161.

6. **Keep the spotlight on your dog:** While it's important to consider how we look in the ring, it's also good to remember that the judge should be judging the dog, not the handler. So keep the spotlight on your dog, as the male dancer does in a "pas de deux" with the ballerina. Practically, that means keeping your dog between you and the judge at all times so you don't block the judge's view.

7. **Rehearse the win photo:** As awards come, you'll be glad to have fantastic win shots to cherish. Practice stacking your dog in his best show pose—balanced, alert, and expressive. Think how you'll stand and hold the leash (observe skilled handlers for inspiration). Train him to pose in a timely manner, considering the judge's schedule. Photographers typically offer valuable tips to enhance your shots. After a quick brush to ensure your doggie shines, think—Stand, Stay, Smile, Photo! Using a mirror for practice helps.

8. **Smile now and then.** Yes, competing with your dog can be serious and stressful, but don't be afraid to smile now and then. Have fun with your partner-pooch, and enjoy the show!

Keep in mind, you're on a journey. The presentation of our dogs improves with practice and time. Attending regular handling classes will prove invaluable as you progress on this journey with your dog. There's always room for growth and refinement and something new to discover!

Choose a Show Outfit Wisely

What would a performance be without a few fancy costumes? But before heading out to shop, there are a few essentials to consider. Our wardrobe is similar to the backdrop for a stage—its primary purpose is to keep the spectators' attention focused on the actors and be in harmony with the theme. With that in mind, opt for clothes/colors/shoes/jewelry that won't upstage your dog, interfere with his movement, hinder the judge's ability to judge accurately, or detract from the presentation at large. Balance formality with functionality.

Here are a few things to consider when shopping for show clothes:

- **The level of decorum:** A dog show is typically a formal competition, so you'll want to respect the level of decorum. Some shows also set guidelines for what is and isn't acceptable. Come prepared.

- **Typical styles:** Dress skirts for women (dress pants are acceptable); dress pants or suits for men.

- **Color:** The color of our clothing is a main factor in the backdrop. For example, showing a black dog while wearing black slacks or a black skirt can destroy the dog's topline for a judge.

- **Clothing:** Functional, wash-and-wear, affordable, pockets to hold dog treats and combs, coverage for bending over and squatting. Avoid clothes that restrict movement or flow excessively.

- **Shoes:** Functional, comfortable, and easy to run or walk alongside your dog in the ring (i.e., flats). Safety is also essential—open-toed shoes or heels could injure you or your dog, and sandals tend to flap, interfering with your dog's movement.

- **Don't skip dress rehearsal:** Practice with your outfit on at home before show day. How does it look with your dog? Is there anything about your outfit distracting from your dog's silhouette or movement? If you're unsure, have someone video you while practicing with your dog.

Don't Forget Playtime

All work and no play make for a bored doggie at home and the show. Mix in some fun amid grooming, training, shopping, and traveling to shows. Active play helps your dog stay mentally healthy, it promotes his physical well-being, alleviates boredom and anxiety, and nurtures his bond with you.

Verify your Dog's Health and Shots

Before leaving for a dog show, it's important to verify your dog is up to date on his shots and healthy for travel. Sometimes, we discover health issues that need attention while grooming our dogs. Consult your vet with any concerns about your dog, such as anal sac issues, ear infections, diarrhea, lethargy, or coughing. Dogs come into contact with lots of people and dogs at shows. Therefore, they must arrive healthy not to infect other dogs. Don't hesitate to withdraw your dog from the competition if there is a health concern.

Make a Packing List

Don't forget to make a packing list. Refer to page 40 for a list of essential items you'll want to take to your event. Missing anything? Refer to page 182 for a list of dog show gear and shopping.

NURTURE A WINNING MINDSET *(see page 46 for positive affirmations.)*

When it comes to competing, mindset is everything. I experienced this as an owner-handler and witnessed it when my daughter competed as a collegiate athlete. Without the right mindset, it's even more challenging to go far in a sport. A winner's mindset rises to the challenge believing they can succeed instead of surrendering at the first hurdle. Developing a winning mindset takes effort. We don't win through osmosis. We win by taking positive steps toward our goals.

Below are 10 tips to help you nurture the champion within you and press onward and upwards!

1. **Define your goals:** Winning-minded people set specific goals for the future, both short and long-term, and commit to achieving them. Create a goal-oriented daily routine to keep moving forward. Integrate these goals into your *dog show calendar* to stay on track. More on goal setting on page 164.

2. **Get out of your comfort zone:** Big goals can make us uneasy. A winning mindset rises to the challenge and takes the necessary steps to move forward, even when uncomfortable. With time and experience, what once made us nervous is no longer such a big deal.

3. **Nurture a positive self-image:** Winning-minded individuals accept themselves as they are (no negative self-talk), prioritize growth, and acknowledge their potential. This approach applies to our show dogs too. We embrace them as-is, improve what we can, and see their potential. Think positive thoughts about yourself and your dog. Use affirmations (p. 46) to nurture your self-image and build confidence during training and shows. Write your affirmations in your dog show log in this book.

4. **Maintain self-discipline:** Showing dogs takes effort. There are moments when grooming, attending handling class, or early morning drives to distant shows seem daunting. A winning mindset commits to a plan, even when it's hard. Life seems to reward those who delay gratification and stick to their goals.

5. **Keep an attitude of gratitude:** The dog show world can get kind of crazy. So many highs and lows, dreams fulfilled, and others crushed, like when our dogs fall ill or pass over rainbow bridge. It's natural to feel down at times. A winning mindset keeps an attitude of gratitude even when it's hard. "Gratitude unlocks the fullness of life. It turns what we have into enough, and more" (Melodie Bettie).

6. **Be flexible:** Expecting things to work out a certain way and only being satisfied when they go that way can cause us a lot of unhappiness. Keeping a flexible mindset lessens disappointments and increases contentment. A winning mindset adjusts to new situations and outcomes, embraces life's uncertainties, and turns obstacles into opportunities for personal growth!

7. **Be curious:** Learning is a life-long process, and the desire for continuing education will propel a person from ordinary to exceptional. Winning-minded people thrive on curiosity, consistently ask questions, and explore better ways of doing things. When a problem arises, they become part of the solution.

8. **Be optimistic:** The dog show journey can get bumpy, leaving us discouraged. A winning mindset is a hopeful mindset. Stay positive while doing your very best to succeed. And if things don't go as you'd hoped, remember, it's a journey. Have faith that your big day is just around the bend. "You win or you learn" (J.J.Clark, Olympic Coach).

9. **Be patient:** Succeeding at dog showing mirrors a marathon more than a swift sprint to success. Will we be like the rabbit in the story of "The Rabbit and the Turtle," dashing off the starting blocks full of pride and zeal, yet quickly running out of steam, winded and wanting to stop? Or, will we be like the turtle, moving steadily, step by step, pacing ourselves, never quitting despite the challenges? Winning-minded

people embrace patience as a friend, knowing she will help them persevere. They set thoughtful goals and take steps (slow and steady) until they come to fruition. As John Wooden, a basketball player and coach, said, "Before success comes patience...when we add to our accomplishments the element of hard work over a long period of time, we'll place a far greater value on the outcome. When we are patient, we'll have a greater appreciation of our success."

10. **Be Kind:** Competition has its low moments. People complain, get stressed, are rubbed the wrong way, and so on. Don't get caught up in the negativity. A winning mindset is kind to all, win or lose. Kind words and gestures demonstrate good sportsmanship, build camaraderie, and benefit the show at large. Even our smallest acts can transform the atmosphere making the show a happier place. No doubt, our dogs also appreciate kind gestures and gentle voices. Being kind also means being kind to yourself, which brings me to the last pre-show tip—take care of yourself too.

TAKE CARE OF YOURSELF TOO

Imagine being the leading partner in a ballroom dance. If you're not feeling well at an event or your head is not in the right place, your partner pooch is probably feeling it on the other end of the leash, which can affect his performance. Below are 7 self-care tips to help you prepare for the big day, lead well, and enjoy the show. **I'm not a doctor. If you have concerns about your health, don't hesitate to consult your physician.**

1. **Get enough rest:** It's tempting to stay up late before a show fussing with dog grooming, packing, etc. But getting enough sleep is essential to be alert while traveling to shows and participating in events.

2. **Stay hydrated:** Canine sporting events are typically long days. Many are also outdoors under the heat of the sun. Pack enough water bottles for you, your family, and your dogs. Stay hydrated.

3. **Eat balanced:** With all the dog show "to-do's," we often skimp on healthy meals. Sweets and fast food have their place, but when we're at a four-day show circuit, and that's all we eat, well, it can have some effects . . . enough said. Plan ahead. Bring a cooler. Pack some healthy snacks and home-cooked meals. Take time at the show to sit, relax, and eat while enjoying the company of friends.

4. **Stay fit:** We all want a fit dog to show, but what about us? Are we taking time to exercise or stretch? It will be easier for our dog to move out and gait well if we keep up. Staying fit can also reduce the risk of injury (i.e., back/knee issues). Consider including exercise in your weekly dog training routine (i.e., a brisk walk with your pooch). Ask your doctor about an exercise plan.

5. **Slow down:** We tend to rush and run while preparing for a show. That's when things are forgotten, or we might hurt ourselves. Plan ahead for the show, so you can take your time at home, drive safely, and walk calmly to your ring. Your dog will also appreciate a calmer person on the other end of the leash.

6. **Wag more worry less:** Life can be filled with care, and we can, unintentionally, bring those cares into the ring. Unburden your mind. Let go of the past, embrace the present, laugh more, and enjoy the show. *And when life gets you down, hug your dog.* Remember, despite our best efforts, releasing worries can prove challenging. Be patient with yourself and those around you. Often, we're unaware of the battles people (or doggies) are fighting.

7. **Be wise:** Last but not least, if, for any reason, you need to change your plans and not go to a show you entered (bad weather, your health, dog not feeling well, other), it's perfectly alright. Be wise. Stay well.

WRAP YOURSELF IN THE COZY BLANKET OF SELF-CARE, A GENTLE REMINDER THAT YOU DESERVE THE SAME COMFORT AS YOUR FURRY COMPANIONS!

SET GOALS FOR YOUR DOG SHOW JOURNEY

What is a goal? A plan or target where you hope to be in the future. Goals are generally categorized into long and short-term goals. Short-term goals serve as stepping stones to long-term goals. How you structure goals is a personal choice. The main idea is to create a plan and steadily move forward.

- **Long-term goals** are your far-off plans. For example: Where do you see yourself in the dog world five to ten years down the line? This could involve aiming to become a judge, mentoring newcomers in the sport, or establishing a successful breeding program.

- **Short-term goals** are typically things you aim to achieve within the current year. For instance, training your dog to free stack or improving your grooming skills for shows. You can even break short-term goals into more manageable *"weekly goals,"* such as committing to attend handling class. You can also write a *"show day goal"* for added focus and calm during an event.

- **Why set goals?** Setting goals can: (1) Give you a clear purpose. (2) Help you stay focused and motivated. (3) Give a sense of personal satisfaction. (4) Add clarity when making decisions. (5) Help you assess your progress. (6) Motivate you to reach your full potential!

- **What if I take a step backward?** Don't be discouraged if you take a few steps back now and then. That's all part of the journey to help you tighten ship and move forward stronger and better.

- **How many goals should I set?** If too many flowers in your garden are squished together, none may come to bloom. Experts have differing views on how many is the correct number of goals to set. Experience tells me if I set 1-3 goals, I am more likely to achieve them than if I set 5-10 goals.

- **Stay balanced:** Goal setting applies to many areas of life—career, financial, fitness, family, spiritual, and dog showing. It's important to remember that a balanced life is a happier life. Thus it's a good idea to make goals in various areas of life. Rank your goals in order of importance and allot time accordingly.

HOW TO USE THE DARING GOALS WORKSHEET

"Daring Goals" was designed to complement the book's theme of aiming high to help you achieve your dog-showing dreams. The acronym (D.A.R.I.N.G.) will guide you in creating goals that are *Detailed, Achievable, Reasonable, Inspiring, Needful, and Gratifying,* aligning with your journey.

1. **Print and make copies** to use while working on writing your goals. Use the worksheet to help you reflect and craft your weekly, short-term, or long-term goals. Keep in mind that goals often evolve as we grow—no worries. Just grab another worksheet and revise your goals as needed.

2. **Start by writing your initial goal,** even if not worded exactly how you'd like. As you work through the worksheet, you'll have the opportunity to refine and create a more polished statement. Try to keep goal statements short using everyday language that's easy to recall.

3. **Keep your goals visible.** Place your goals worksheet in a spot you'll see it often to remember your goals and stay motivated.

4. **Incorporate your goals** into your monthly show planner and competition log in the space provided.

5. **Organize your worksheets** in a folder to review and evaluate your progress.

6. **Set a Target Date:** Write down and commit to a date to achieve your goal. *Go get em!*

SETTING GOALS AND SEEING THEM THROUGH CULTIVATES A WINNING MINDSET.

Print this worksheet out to reuse. Place where you'll see it often to be inspired!

MY *DARING GOALS* WORKSHEET

INITIAL GOAL: Write the initial goal you have in mind, even if it's not worded exactly how you'd like.

_____

DETAILED: What specifically do I want to accomplish? Who needs to be included?

_____

_____

ACHIEVABLE: Do I have the skills required to achieve this goal? If not, what specific steps can I take to acquire the needed skills? What is the date I plan to meet this goal?

_____

_____

REASONABLE: Am I able to commit to this goal, given my current situation? If not, what changes can I make to my lifestyle and/or daily routine to help bring this goal within reach?

_____

_____

INSPIRING: How does this goal move me out of my comfort zone and closer to my greater goals?

_____

_____

NEEDFUL: Why am I setting this goal now? Is it aligned with my overall objectives?

_____

_____

GRATIFYING: Is this goal worth my time and effort to achieve? How will it improve my life?

_____

_____

MY DARING GOAL: Review what you've written and craft a new goal statement based on your answers.

_____

_____

I will achieve this goal by _____

SHOWTIME TIPS

It's showtime! So you've practiced and prepped for the big show day. What now?

The night before . . .

- **Verify your packing list:** Are all show brushes, leads, entry forms, judging schedule, etc. packed?

- **Set your alarm:** Can you imagine how awful it would be after all your hard work to sleep in? Set your alarm to give yourself enough time for last-minute show preps (grooming touch-ups, meal prep, etc.).

- **Map your route:** The day before the show, verify the route to your venue, time to get there, and forecast.

Arriving at the event . . .

- **Arrive early:** Get to the venue early enough to get your dog settled. Your pooch will appreciate a little walk to potty and stretch his legs, especially after a long drive.

- **Set up:** Find a convenient, safe, shady spot to set up and do last-minute grooming touch-ups. If you've reserved a grooming spot, even better. Note: If your show girl is in heat, try to set up at a distance from male dogs.

- **Check in:** Arrive early at your ring and check in with the ring steward. Give your dog's name and number, and they will give you your armband.

- **Consider Videoing:** Ask someone to video you in the ring using a smartphone, iPad, etc. This way, you can study it later for insight into the overall presentation of your dog.

- **Observe the ring:** Before you show, hang out ringside, observing the judge you'll show to. As they assess breeds before yours, watch how they examine dogs and manage the ring. Do they request exhibitors to show the dog's bite or take a look themselves? Are they asking for an "up and back" or another pattern? Is the judge giving any special instructions? Observing your judge will help you be prepared.

- **Warm up your dog:** At some point before entering the ring, you'll want to warm up your dog (as appropriate for your breed). A brisk walk near the ring will do to stretch his legs and get him focused.

- **Remember the stress factor:** Stress and competition often go hand in hand. If you're feeling stressed at a dog show, consider that many of your competitors may feel the same. Be mindful of the "stress factor" ringside and in the ring when some unfortunate altercations sometimes happen. Keep calm and carry on. Don't take things too personally.

- **Have a backup:** If you're showing more than one dog and they both win their classes, you'll need someone to bring one of them back in the ring. Have a backup handler ready, just in case.

Entering the ring . . .

- **Stay tuned:** As ring time approaches, stay tuned. You won't want to miss your number called and lose your chance to show. If you're a tad late, you may still be able to ask permission to enter the ring.

- **Pay attention to instructions:** Listen carefully for any instructions when in the ring. For example, the ring steward or judge may ask you to go around the ring and stop at a specific part of the ring. Judges certainly appreciate it when exhibitors follow their instructions. Everything runs more smoothly.

- **Keep calm:** Before entering the ring, take a few deep breaths to cultivate calmness. Dogs pick up on the calm, which helps them too. If your dog needs a little encouragement to move out with tail wagging, talk happily to your dog as you enter the ring.

- **Stay alert:** Be alert in the ring, similar to driving on the road. Mishaps can happen! For example, the pup ahead of you might suddenly refuse to walk, causing you to hit the brakes. Your puppy may decide it's time to poop. A child may start crying and fussing ringside. Be a reassuring presence for your dog while keeping an appropriate distance from other handlers and their dogs.

- **Keep an eye on the judge:** In larger classes, dogs might spend time waiting and not always maintain a show pose, which is normal. Just watch the judge. When their attention shifts to other dogs, your dog can relax. But when the judge looks your way or approaches your dog, ensure your "star" is stacked pretty, tail wagging, and showing expression. *Here's a tip:* teach your dog a "perk-up word" like "treat" or "cookie" (associate it with a tasty treat when training). Teaching them to "catch" bait is also handy. These keep your dog alert, focused on you, and expressive—perfect for when the judge approaches your dog. You'll also get a more balanced, relaxed "free stack."

- **Show to the end!** Keep your dog showing his best to the very end. It's not over till it's over.

- **Don't leave too soon:** If you got a blue or red ribbon in your class, don't leave until Reserve Winners is awarded. You may need to go back in the ring to compete for Reserve.

When you are done showing . . .

- **Offer congrats:** Graciously accept win or loss, thank the judge, and congratulate the winners.

- **Win photo:** If you win and would like a photo with the judge, find out where and when that takes place. A professional photographer will have a setup you can go to. Or, the photographer may be called to the ring for the picture. Enjoy the moment!

- **Double-check wins and points:** If you win, confirm with the ring steward or at the superintendent's desk that your dog's number was correctly written. Also, verify the total number of dogs that actually participated to confirm your points. Know the point schedule for your breed in the area you showed.

- **Celebrate your dog:** Win or lose, let your dog know he's PAWSOME! Swing by the vendors and offer him something special. Be in the moment with your canine star. Your pup will carry the positive energy forward, radiating a joyful demeanor in the shows ahead!

- **Pause and reflect** on the show experience. What went well? What can you improve? Did you gain new insights about your dog, yourself, or the judging? Were there specific comments from the judge about your dog? Document these valuable takeaways within this log book. Revisit your notes to refine your skills, track your progress and celebrate achievements. **Remember, mistakes aren't failures; they're invaluable teachers who can help you improve.**

- **Revisit goals:** As you progress, you'll want to write new goals and keep moving forward. Use the goal setting worksheet provided on page 165.

At all times at your sporting event . . .

- **Listen to your dog:** With all the "noise" at an event, stay alert to your dog's cues. Is he relaxed, happy, and in good health? Does he appear uneasy or too warm? Be ready to take action. Their wellness is a priority.

ENJOY THE SHOW!

OWNER-HANDLER TIPS

At my first dog show, I recall walking up to a well-dressed, professional-looking lady who had just won and asking for advice. While chatting, I told her she was a superb professional handler, and I enjoyed watching her with her dog. *"You made my day!"* she said with a smile. *"I'm an owner-handler. But thank you!"* Her example inspired me to work hard, overcome shortcomings and present my dogs with excellence. As time went on, I started winning more and gaining confidence. Then one day, while standing ringside after showing my dog, someone mistook me for a professional handler!

Ever since, I have thought to myself that everyone has the possibility of looking like a pro. We just need to work hard, nurture the bond with our dog, and believe we can win too. That said, here are three motivational tips learned along my owner-handler journey.

1. **Brave the work:** The pros work hard, and you can too. Hard work is available to everyone. Dedicate yourself to improving your craft. Create goals and see them through. And never stop learning. Knowledge is everywhere—online, at shows, in training classes, in books, and even in your dog's eyes.

2. **Be aware of the bond:** As an owner-handler, you have a unique opportunity to show off that special connection with your dog, developed through countless hours of training and doing life together. Be aware of the bond in the ring. It can work to your advantage. There's a special beauty about the human-canine bond that calls attention. It reminds the onlooker that, above all, dogs are our closest friends.

3. **Believe you can win:** To believe is to have faith, meaning you see your goal achieved (in your mind's eye) even though it's not yet a reality (positive affirmations can help). This can be hard for owner-handlers. There's an element of insecurity, thinking pros have an advantage. But with experience, insecurity fades, and faith rises. That said, even after years of showing dogs, moments of uncertainty may surface, and that's okay. We can still smile and do our best. That's what matters. That's a winning mindset.

   Believing you can win also means looking the part. Choose your wardrobe wisely. Come with a meticulously groomed dog. Enter the ring prepared and with professionalism, graciously accepting the outcome. Rise to the challenge, and realize your dreams. One day, someone might mistake you for a pro. But it won't be a mistake because you would have earned the part.

   A final thought. Remember, "winning" is more about the journey than the ribbons. If you've given your all, enjoyed your dogs, and grown along the way, you achieved success!

About the AKC National Owner-Handled Series (NOHS)

The National Owner-Handled Series (NOHS) recognizes and celebrates owner-handler exhibitors. Owner-Handlers compete in the regular classes with the NOHS Best of Breed award given following regular judging. To enter the NOHS, check the *owner-handler box* on your entry form. There is no additional fee.

For more on NOHS please visit: www.akc.org/sports/conformation/national-owner-handled-series/

Photo: Memorable owner-handled win. Leila and her dog Toby, with AKC judge Sharon Newcomb.

Part 4
Dog Show Resources

COUNTING AKC CHAMPIONSHIP POINTS

AKC AWARDS AND RIBBONS

AKC TITLES AND MEANINGS

DOG PARTS & MOVEMENT VOCABULARY

COMMON DOG SHOW TERMS

STEPS FOR NEW EXHIBITORS

SPORTSMANSHIP AFFIRMATIONS

SHOW GEAR AND SHOPPING

PET SITTER INSTRUCTION FORM

DOG GROOMING GOAL CALENDAR

RECOMMENDED READING & LINKS

DOG SHOW SAFETY TIPS

No matter how little money and how few possessions you own, having a dog makes you rich.

—Louis Gabin

How to Count Championship Points

How to Count Championship Points, by Laura Reeves, AKC judge, breeder,
host of Pure Dog Talk Podcast, www.PureDogTalk.com

UNDERSTANDING THE CLASSES

All classes are divided by sex and championship status. The non-champion male dogs compete for Winners Dog. The non-champion female dogs compete for Winners Bitch. Only animals awarded Winners Dog and Winners Bitch are eligible to earn points toward their championship status. After that, the Champion animals and the Winners Dog and Winners Bitch compete for Best of Breed.

WHAT ARE THE CLASSES? Class options and order are:

- 6-9 months puppy
- 9-12 months puppy
- 12-18 months
- Novice class (which is designated for dogs that have not won three blue ribbons in another class. It applies to the dog, not the exhibitor).
- Amateur Owner Handler Class (defined by the exhibitor, not the dog).
- American Bred Class (dogs bred in the US).
- Bred By Exhibitor Class (dogs bred by the person showing the dog or an immediate family member).
- Open Class (any animal, any age, any handler).

In certain breeds, classes might also be divided by coat, color, or size. Very seldom will you see entries in every single one of the available classes. The non champion (or class dogs as we call them) males are all judged in class order. The winner of each class remains at ringside to return and compete for Winners Dog. The second place animal in each class (if there is one) ALSO remains handy.

WINNERS DOG

This can sometimes be a little confusing. The steward will call the winners of each class back into the ring — in the reverse order they were judged. The judge will select Winners Dog from the class winners. This is the dog who is awarded championship points (more on this later). Once Winners Dog leaves the ring, if there was a dog that placed second in the winner's class, that dog will be called back in to the ring to be considered for RESERVE Winners Dog. If there was no second place animal, reserve is chosen from the dogs remaining in the ring. Reserve is literally the animal who could be awarded championship points if the Winners animal is deemed ineligible for any reason.

WINNERS BITCH

The female entries go through the same process in order to select Winners Bitch and Reserve Winners Bitch.

BEST OF BREED COMPETITION

All of the champions are called in to the ring, with Winners Dog and Winners Bitch, at the end of the lineup. Generally, the judge will ask for male champions first, female champions next, followed by the winners. This is NOT a given, and how the champions are lined up is completely at the judge's discretion. This is one of the reasons it is smart to watch a ring for a breed or two before yours is judged.

At the end of judging, the judge will line the dogs up in order of their placement . . .

- **Best of Breed** winner is first.
- **Next in line is the Best of Winners**. This is the judge's choice of the best of the class dogs. This award can have bearing when counting points.
- **Next is the Best of Opposite Sex to Best of Breed.** If the judge selects a male dog for Best of Breed, this award is given to a female and vice versa.
- **Finally male and female Select awards** are presented. These awards confer grand champion points and are only available to champion dogs in the ring which did not win Best of Breed or Best of Opposite.

HOW TO COUNT THE POINTS

Points are awarded based on the number of dogs defeated. Dogs can earn from zero to five points at a given dog show. For example, if there is only one class dog and one class bitch entered, there will be no points available. Any time a dog defeats enough animals to earn three, four or five points, it's called a Major. All dogs have to earn two major wins and accumulate 15 total points to be awarded championship status.

How many championship points are awarded is based upon three factors: Breed, sex and area of the country.

Example: German Wirehaired Pointers in Oregon with an entry of four class dogs and seven class bitches — both Winners Dog and Winners Bitch will earn three points for a major. In other areas of the country, that might equal only two points. If you're showing a Golden Retriever, it requires 24 bitches to earn a three point major.

AKC's Point Schedule covers all 15 divisions of the country. This schedule is adjusted in May every year. So what constitutes a major on May 1 might well not count on May 15.

Example-Schedule of Points for Division 15-From a previous year.

	1 Point Dogs	1 Point Bitches	2 Points Dogs	2 Points Bitches	3 Points Dogs	3 Points Bitches	4 Points Dogs	4 Points Bitches	5 Points Dogs	5 Points Bitches
Brittany's	2	2	5	5	7	7	9	10	13	18
Lagotti Romagnoli.	2	2	3	3	4	4	5	5	6	6
Pointers	2	2	3	4	4	5	5	6	6	7
Pointers (German Shorthaired) . . .	2	2	4	4	5	7	7	9	10	13
Pointers (German Wirehaired). . . .	2	2	3	4	4	7	5	8	10	9

THE BASICS:

- Make sure you know the point schedule for your breed in the area where you show dogs.
- Make sure you pay attention to the number of dogs actually IN the ring. Just because the dogs are entered doesn't count! If they don't show up, it can drastically change the points available.
- If you got a blue ribbon or a red ribbon in your class, don't leave until the purple and white ribbon is handed out!
- In all cases, if you are the winner, verify with the ring steward or the superintendent that the judge wrote down your dog's number properly. Verify the number of dogs actually in attendance.
- You can do this most easily by asking the superintendent to see the "tear sheets" from the judge's book. These are always available to exhibitors, usually within an hour or two of the end of judging of your breed.

So there you go. You are prepared for the dog show with hard facts about the gobbledygook that was stressing you out. This way, you can focus on your dog and making every second in the ring count.

AKC Awards & Ribbons

COMMON AKC ABBREVIATIONS USED FOR WINS AT CONFORMATION SHOWS:

WD-Winners Dog: The winning male dog chosen over all the regular classes (non-champions) of his sex.

WB-Winners Bitch: The winning female dog chosen over all the regular classes (non-champions) of her sex.

RWD/RWB-Reserve Winners Dog/Reserve Winners Bitch: Runner up to the winners dog and bitch. If the winner becomes ineligible for the award, then the runner up will receive the points awarded from that show.

BOW-Best of Winners: Best between Winners Dog and Winners Bitch in the class competition.

BOB-Best of Breed: Defeats all dogs present in the breed; will go on to the Group competition.

BOS-Best of Opposite Sex: Best of the breed in the sex opposite to that which won Best of Breed.

SD-Select Dog: Second best male champion present in a breed.

SB-Select Bitch: Second best female champion present in a breed.

GR-Group: The Best of Breed winner advances to group competition to compete against other breeds in the same group. The #1 dog in the group goes on to compete for Best In Show.

BIS-Best In Show: Defeats all dogs present at an All-Breed show.

BISS-Best in Show Specialty: Where only dogs of the same breed are competing in conformation.

SOME OTHER WIN ABBREVIATIONS AT SHOWS INCLUDE:

Award of Merit (AOM); Award of Excellence (AOE), Best Bred by Exhibitor (BBBE); Best Puppy In Breed (BPIB); Best Puppy In Group (BPIG); Best Puppy In Show (BPIS); Best In Specialty Sweepstakes (BISS)

COLORS AND RIBBONS FOR AKC CONFORMATION SHOWS

Blue: First place in any regular class. Also awarded to the winner of each group competition, usually in the form of a "rosette".

Red: Second place in each class. Also awarded for second place in each group competition, usually in the form of a "rosette".

Yellow: Third place in each class. Also awarded for third place in each group competition, usually in the form of a "rosette".

White: Fourth place in each class. Also awarded for fourth in each group competition, usually in the form of a "rosette".

Purple: Winners of the Winners Dog and Winners Bitch classes. Championship points can be earned in these classes.

Purple and White: Reserve Winners, that is, the runners-up to the winner of the Winners Dog and Winners Bitch classes.

Blue and White: Best of Winners, that is, the better of the Winners Dog and Winners Bitch winners.

Purple and Gold: Awarded to the "Best of Breed" in each breed competition. This ribbon allows advancement to the Group competition.

Red and White: Best of Opposite Sex, meaning the best dog of the breed that is the opposite sex of the best of breed winner.

Light Blue and White: Awarded to the Select Dog and Select Bitch in the BOB competition. Points go towards the Grand Championship Title.

Red, White and Blue: Awarded at the end of each show to the ultimate winner, the BEST IN SHOW!

COLORS AND RIBBONS FOR AKC NATIONAL OWNER-HANDLED SERIES, NOHS

"The purpose of the AKC National Owner-Handled Series (NOHS) is to recognize and showcase the quality dogs being exhibited by owner/handlers and to provide a venue for the owner/handlers to compete against their peers." (1) The NOHS occurs after Best of Breed judging in each breed ring. Dogs ranking in the top ten for their breed during the qualifying period are allowed to compete in this competition. For more on the NOHS please visit: www.akc.org/sports/conformation/national-owner-handled-series/

The AKC point scale and ribbon colors for NOHS are:

PLACEMENT	POINTS	RIBBON COLOR
Owner-Handled Best in Show	100	Turquoise
Owner-Handled Reserve Best in Show	75	Light Green
Owner-Handled Group 1	30	Neon Pink
Owner-Handled Group 2	20	Neon Green
Owner-Handled Group 3	15	Teal
Owner-Handled Group 4	10	Cream
Owner-Handled Best of Breed	5	Maroon
Owner-Handled Best of Breed at National Specialty	10	Maroon

Many other ribbons exist in specialty shows, etc.

(1) www.akc.org/sports/conformation/national-owner-handled-series/akc-national-owner-handled-series-best-practices/

AKC Titles & Meanings

Below are the most common abbreviations for wins and titles earned. For a complete list and to learn more about each title please visit www.akc.org/sports/titles-and-abbreviations/.

CONFORMATION TITLES (from the www.akc.org website)

CH-Champion of Record: Earned by gaining 15 points with two major wins. A "Major" win is worth 3, 4, or 5 points by the AKC point system. The majors must be won under different judges, and at least one other judge must award some of the remaining points — so you need to win under at least three different judges. Points awarded are determined by the number of other entries the winning dog defeats.

GCH-Grand Champion: AKC requires a dog to obtain a total of 25 points with 3 major wins (3 points or higher) to become a GCH. Majors must be won under three different judges, and at least one other judge must award some of the remaining points, meaning you need to win under at least four different judges. Also, one Champion must be defeated at three of these shows. To be eligible for GCH competition, a dog must be (1) a champion of record or (2) have been transferred to BOB based on the owner's record of having completed the requirements for a CH title.

There are five levels of GCH achievable: 1. Grand Champion (GCH) 2. Grand Champion Bronze (GCHB) 3. Grand Champion Silver (GCHS) 4. Grand Champion Gold (GCHG) 5. Grand Champion Platinum (GCHP#).

CM#-Certificate of Merit: The CM suffix title is an introductory title to AKC conformation events. Winners of the Best of Breed in each of the Miscellaneous breeds will be awarded points towards the CM title. AKC requires a dog to obtain 15 points to earn a CM.

OTCH – OBEDIENCE TRIAL CHAMPION

To earn an obedience title, the dog must have a passing score of 50% of possible points or better, and an overall passing score at three different competitions under three different judges.

CD – Companion Dog (First Level Obedience Competition, basic obedience exercises).

CDX – Companion Dog Excellent (Intermediate Level Obedience Competition, more advanced obedience work).

UD – Utility Dog (Advanced Level Obedience Competition, difficult obedience work, including hand signals).

UDX – The highest obedience degree AKC presently awards.

AGILITY	HERDING	TRACKING
NA-Novice Agility	HT- Herding Tested	TD-Tracking Dog
OA-Open Agility	PT- PreTrial Tested	TDX-Tracking Dog Excellent
AX-Agility Excellent	HS- Herding Started	VST-Variable Surface Tracking
MX-Master Agility Excellent	HI-Herding Intermediate	
NAJ-Novice Agility Jumper	HX-Herding Excellent	
OAJ-Open Agility Jumper	HCh-Herding Champion	
EAJ-Excellent Agility Jumper		

HEALTH CERTIFICATIONS, HEART, EYES, HIP, OTHER.

OVC – Ontario Veterinary College

OVC Hip Certification.

OFA – Orthopedic Foundation for Animals.

OFA Hip Certifications -Excellent, Good, or Fair.

OFA – Elbow Certification – only one grade recognized as normal.

OFA is also now doing certifications for other canine health concerns. Check with OFA for more information.

CERF – Canine Eye Registry Foundation-certified to have normal eyes. Re-certification is done annually.

vWD – Von Willebrands Disease free-meaning the dog has been tested and found free of vWD, a bleeding disorder, vWD free ratings are often given with a percentage listed. For the best information on Von Willebrand's Disease, contact Dr Jean Dodds, who is the leading research specialist in blood disorders.

For Breed Health Testing Requirements visit www.akc.org. Type in search bar: "Breed Health Testing Requirements."

AKC UNOFFICIAL TITLES

CGC – Canine Good Citizen

ROM – Register of Merit – Dog or bitch must earn a number of points specified by the DPCA rules, and also meet the numbers of champion and major pointed progeny required by DPCA. Requirements for bitches are less than the requirements for dogs because males have the opportunity to produce a far larger number of offspring.

ROMC – Canadian ROM

ROM/C – Dog has earned an American and Canadian ROM.

TT – Temperament Tested

TC – Temperament Certified

AOE – Award of Excellence-Dog must meet qualifications in conformation, obedience, and also be OFA'd to earn this award.

RTD – Registered Therapy Dog

TDI - Passed Therapy Dog International's testing

NEW COMPETITIONS are being added and rules for competitions change. For the most up-to-date rules and regulations, check with the AKC and the DPCA.

AKC TITLES & PROGRAMS TO DO FROM HOME: www.akc.org/expert-advice/sports/akc-titles-programs-can-home/

Dog Parts & Movement Vocabulary

A well-made dog will move with all parts working together correctly to form a balanced silhouette while standing and on the move. This list is not exhaustive. Excellent learning material is available online. The best place to learn, however, is while watching various dog breeds standing and on the move at shows. You'll be training your eye to recognize the faults and virtues of dogs, with breed type in mind.

Standard: The official, written description of what constitutes the perfect conformation characteristics of a particular breed.

Conformation: The form and structure, make and shape; arrangement of the parts in conformance with breed standards. (1)

Condition: Health as shown by the coat, skin, general appearance, and behavior. (1)

Angulation: The angles created by bones meeting at their given joints. (1)

Soundness: A dog considered to have mental and physical well-being. "A sound dog."

Head: The overall shape of the head, including the eyes, ears, and head planes. The head is a distinguishing feature of a breed, influencing his overall appearance, meaning breed type.

Head Planes: Viewed in profile, the contours of the top portion of the skull from occiput to stop, and the foreface from stop to tip of the nose. (1)

Breed Type: This means a dog looks like its breed, per breed standard. There are variations in "type" because some dogs come closer to their standard than others.

Body Shape: A breeds body proportions, size, and shape. Most dogs are described as either square, nearly square, long, or rectangular.

Front Assembly: Begins at top of shoulder blades (withers); includes forearm, front legs, pasterns and feet.

Lay-Back: The tilt of the shoulder blades towards the back (rump) of the dog. Lay-In is the tilt of the shoulder blades toward each other.

Rear: It involves the vital hip joint which connects the femur to the tibia and fibula at the knee joint. It gives the dog forward thrust and drive. (2)

Body Length: Distance from the prosternum (front portion of the breastbone) to the posterior portion of the pelvic girdle. (1)

Hock: The collection of bones of the hind leg forming the joint between the second thigh and the metatarsus; the dog's true heel. (1) Hocking out: when hocks are spread. Hocks "well let down": when hocks are close to the ground. Cow-Hocked: hocks turning in, accompanied by toeing out of rear feet.

Bad Mouth: Crooked teeth; when the mouth is closed, upper and lower teeth do not line up according to the standard of the breed. (1)

Topline: From the base of a dog's neck to the base of the tail—withers, back, loin, croup. See diagram.

Tail Set: How the base of the tail is set on the rump. See diagram.

Crabbing (side-winding): When a dog moves with its body at an angle to the line of travel.

Elbows Out: Turning out or off from the body; not held close. (1)

Movement: The judge evaluates movement in three ways in the ring— from the side, going and coming. A dog's movement is a good indicator of structure and condition. *See online articles, reference 2 below.*

Pacing: A lateral gait that tends to promote a rolling motion of the body. The left foreleg and left hind leg advance in unison, then the right foreleg and right hind leg. (1)

Gait: The pattern of footsteps at different speeds, distinguished by a specific rhythm and footfall. Dogs have 4 main gaits—walk, trot, canter, gallop. The Amble is a transitional gate between walk and trot. Different breeds are shown at different gaits (i.e., Trotting dog/German Shepherd, Galloping dog/Greyhound).

Walk: Gaiting pattern in which three legs support the body at all times, each foot lifting from the ground one at a time in regular sequence. (1)

Trot: A rhythmic two-beat diagonal gait in which the feet at diagonal opposite ends of the body strike the ground together, i.e., right hind with left front and left hind with right front. (1)

Canter: A gait with three beats to each stride, two legs moving separately and two as a diagonal pair. (1)

Gallop: Fastest of dog gaits; has a four-beat rhythm and often an extra period of suspension during which the body is propelled through the air with all four feet off the ground. (1)

Reach of Front: Length of forward stride taken by forelegs. (1)

Drive: A solid thrusting of the hindquarters, denoting sound locomotion. (1)

Balance: When all the parts of the dog, moving or standing, produce a harmonious image. (1)

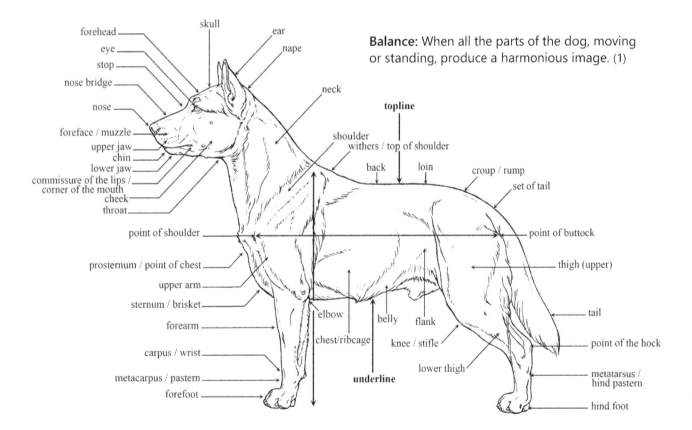

Dog parts surface anatomy image used with permission from the FCI, Federation Cynologique Internationale website.

(1) The AKC glossary www.akc.org/about/glossary/

(2) Breeding Better Dogs: https://breedingbetterdogs.com/article/ structure-and-movement-pt-1 (also part 2)

Common Dog Show Terms

These are some terms you'll hear at shows. You will undoubtedly hear many more; if you're not already, you'll soon be fluent in dog show lingo! AKC Awards and abbreviations vocabulary-page 172.

Dog: Although used for both sexes of the canine species, for show/breeding purposes, it is the male.

Bitch: A female dog is known as a bitch.

Purebred Dog: Having both parents of the same breed or variety. Typically has a documented pedigree in a stud book, and may be registered with a breed club that may also be part of a national kennel club.

A Class Dog: A dog competing in the classes that is not already a champion.

A Special: A dog that is already a Champion competing for Best of Breed only. A Special cannot compete in the classes where points are earned because a Champion has already earned them.

Pedigree: The written record of a dog's family tree of three or more generations.

Handler: The person presenting the dog in the ring, either its owner, breeder, or a hired professional.

Judge: Official approved by the AKC to evaluate dogs in specific AKC events. In conformation, this is a purebred dog expert.

Bred By Exhibitor: A conformation class in which breeders showcase the dogs they've bred. In the class, the breeder must be the one showing the dog. They cannot be taken into the ring by another handler.

Breeder-Owner-Handler: Someone who exhibits, owns, and handles the dog they bred.

Miscellaneous Class: Transitory class for breeds desiring to advance to full AKC recognition. (1)

Armband: A piece of paper worn by an exhibitor (on his or her arm), carrying a number corresponding to the number in the show judge's reference book.

Catalog: Document you can obtain at a dog show containing the name and number of each dog entered, the name of owner/breeder/handler, and the sire and dam names.

Judging Schedule: Lists the time and location of the classes for each breed and who will be judging.

Premium List: Publication stating the date and location of a dog show, the club hosting the show, classes, awards, the judges, and information on fees and entry forms.

Closing Date: The final day you can submit a show entry. Closing is usually 3-4 weeks before a show.

Baiting: Using liver or some treat or toy to get the dog's attention and have him look alert when showing.

Tack Box: Container used to hold your tack—your dog's grooming tools, leads, collars, etc.

Stacking: (Hand stacking) Physically posing the dog's legs and body to create a pleasing picture. (Free Stacking) Using subtle signals (cannot touch dog) to tell the dog where to put his feet and center of gravity.

Super: Short for superintendent—the organization that runs the event for the club hosting the show.

Match Show (or Fun Match): Usually an informal dog show where no championship points are awarded.

Bench Show: A dog show where dogs are kept in an assigned area when not being shown in competition so that attendees can see the dogs up close and talk to owners, handlers, and breeders.

Westminster KC: "The Garden." Prestigious all-breed dog show held annually in New York. It is America's second-longest continuously held sporting event, behind only the Kentucky Derby. It is a benched show.

Crufts: An international dog show held annually in the United Kingdom. Largest show of its kind in the world.

Points: Credits earned (points) toward a championship.

Major: When a dog has defeated many other dogs at a show, earning 3-5 points towards its championship.

Finish: *To finish* means a dog earned enough points to be awarded the title of Champion of Record.

Winners: Non-champions who earn championship points in the classes. (Winners Dog/Winners Bitch).

DQ: Short for "disqualification," A DQ trait, if present on a dog, immediately eliminates him from competition.

Best: Term used for "Best in Show." *"What time are they doing Best?"*

Groups: Where Best of Breed winners compete in their respective group. There are seven groups recognized by AKC and CKC: Hound, Sporting, Non-Sporting, Working, Herding, Terrier, and Toy. Dogs are categorized by functional similarities. The winner of each group competes for **Best in Show.**

Trial: means "competition." A commonly used term at a canine sporting event.

Conformation: The official word for "dog shows."

Dog Fancier: If you get really involved in canine sports, you might call yourself a "fancier."

Competitors: Also called "exhibitors."

Junior Handler: A person competing in Junior Showmanship Competition. A Junior is a youngster between the ages of 10 and 18, competing with others their own age at various AKC events. Unlike a conformation show, it is the young handlers dog handling skills being judged, not their dogs.

Photo: Our young son at his first dog show as a Junior Handler presenting our ruby Cavalier King Charles Spaniel.

(1) The AKC glossary www.akc.org/about/glossary/

Steps for New Exhibitors

- Make sure your dog is registered with the AKC or the registry your dog is affiliated with.

- Be sure your dog is current on vaccinations and healthy for travel.

- Join your breed's Parent Club or a Local Specialty club in your area.

- Become familiar with the AKC show rules and regulations for dog shows, or the rules of the organization you will be involved with.

- Read the *AKC Code of Sportsmanship* at akc.org or the club's sportsmanship code where you are involved.

- Learn your dog's breed standard.

- Attend handling classes with your dog. These help with proper techniques for presenting your dog in the ring and general dog show training. Young dogs benefit especially from this early training.

- Learn and practice proper grooming techniques before the show, with the breed standard in mind.

- Attend some dog shows simply as a spectator to observe the presentation and judging of your breed. Obtain a Judging Program and familiarize yourself with what it looks like.

- Wear comfortable shoes. Bring a chair, as seating is usually limited. You might want to plan some shade covering if it's an outdoor show.

- Decide if you or a professional handler will be presenting your dog.

- Don't be afraid to ask questions to the breeder of your dog, club members, and experts in your breed.

- If the grooming area is open to spectators, talk with professional groomers to get tips on grooming.

- Do not pet a dog (or offer treats) without first asking for permission. The dog may have just been groomed in preparation for being judged.

- Do not approach owners/handlers as they're about to enter the ring. They are focused on the task at hand.

- Visit the vendors and information booths. Many club booths offer helpful information to the general public. Vendors can also guide you in choosing excellent dog show products to keep your dog looking its best.

- **Relax. Have fun. Enjoy the reason for being there—those beautiful doggies.**

For more information on how to get started showing your dog, visit www.akc.org/sports/conformation/get-started/

❧ ❧ Sportsmanship Affirmations ❧ ❧

Sportsmanship can be summed up by how we treat each other, i.e., being kind and respectful, whether we like the outcome of a show or not. Achieving true success in our events involves embracing principles of good sportsmanship. Please take a moment to read the *AKC Code of Sportsmanship* from their website. It speaks to the heart of purebred dogs and applies to people in all roles at shows—exhibitors, judges, AKC officials, etc. Below I've written it in the first person to use as affirmations to help nurture a sportsman's attitude.

I AM A GOOD SPORTSMAN: (Adapted from the AKC Code of Sportsmanship www.akc.org, written from the perspective of an exhibitor showing in conformation dog shows).

- I respect the history, traditions, and integrity of the sport of purebred dogs.

- I am committed to the values of fair play, courtesy, vigorous competition, and winning and losing with grace.

- I refuse to compromise my commitment and obligation to the sport of purebred dogs by injecting personal advantage into my decisions and behavior.

- I decline to enter or exhibit under a judge where it might reasonably appear that the judge's placements could be based on something other than the merits of my dogs.

- I refuse to compromise the impartiality of a judge.

- I respect the AKC bylaws, rules, regulations, and policies governing the sport of purebred dogs.

- I find that vigorous competition and civility are not inconsistent, and I appreciate the merit of my competition and the efforts of my competitors.

- I welcome, encourage, and support all newcomers to the sport.

- I deal fairly with all those I work with in the sport.

- I am willing to share honest and open appraisals of my breeding stock's strengths and weaknesses.

- I spurn the opportunity to take personal advantage of positions offered or bestowed upon me.

- I always consider as paramount the welfare of my dogs.

- I refuse to embarrass the sport, the American Kennel Club (or any other club I am involved with) while taking part in the sport.

Sportsmanship is the golden rule of sports—Always treat others how you wish to be treated.

❦ ❀ Show Gear and Shopping ❀ ❦

A gear packing checklist is found on page 40, to print and reuse for each show.

DOG GROOMING TOOLS AND SUPPLIES

- Comb/brush, appropriate for your dog's coat type (i.e. slicker brush, pin brush)
- Spray bottle
- Grooming/conditioning spray
- Shampoo/conditioner/waterless shampoo is also handy at shows for quick clean-ups.
- Nail clippers
- Baby wipes/Paper towels

- Scissors/clippers
- Rubber bands (for long-coated breeds)
- Ear Snoods (for breeds with long ears)
- Tack box/Grooming bag
- Dryer: Forced air dryers are the most common type used by groomers and dog show exhibitors.
- Towels: i.e. Super absorbent dog drying towels, drying coat.
- Sturdy Grooming Table and Grooming Arm

SHOW LEAD

A show lead is typically one-piece with a loop and an adjustable slide that functions as the collar. This is slightly different than a standard leash/collar for daily use. Most exhibitors have several leads on hand at shows. There are several types. Try different ones until you find one that works for your dog. Some leads help more with training your dog to keep its head held nicely while gaiting and stacking. Once you find the right lead, practice with it so your dog will get comfortable with it on.

- **Resco "all in one"** style collar with lead: The Resco has a loop with a slider to keep it snug on the dog's neck. Often used with smaller breeds.

- **Martingale lead:** These leads keep your dog's head from slipping out, but don't tighten around the neck like a choke chain. Often used with medium size breeds.

- **Chain and Show Lead:** Often used for larger breeds.

Tips for fitting a show collar and lead: www.cherrybrook.com/how-to-select-the-appropriate-show-collar-and-lead/

CONTAINMENT: CRATES/CRATE SUPPLIES/X-PENS

- **Crate:** i.e., open-wire crate, fold-up canvas, heavy-duty plastic crate . . .
- **Crate cover** or sheet (make sure the crate is well ventilated): These offer your dog some privacy and peace and quiet at shows.
- **Crate bedding:** Measure your crate to find specially made crate pads to fit. A soothing blanket is nice too.
- **Crate fan:** (They attach to the crate.) In hot weather, these help your dog stay cool while traveling and at shows.
- **Crate dolly:** For ease with moving crates with dogs. Don't forget the bungee cords to tie things down.
- **Trolley:** Another option for moving crates is a trolley. These are basically crates on wheels and fold up for car travel.
- **Foldable X-pen:** These pens allow dogs more room to move about and stretch their legs.
- **Ground Cover/shade cover:** To keep dogs clean; to protect from the heat of the sun.

FOOD AND WATER

Bring dog food, water, and your dog's bowls. You can purchase water bottles that attach to crates. These are useful for giving dogs a drink without their ears or feathering getting wet. Sometimes exhibitors also use a spray bottle with water to offer their dog a quick refresher, for example, right before entering the ring. Regarding food, show week is not the time to switch brands. It might upset your dog's tummy.

BAIT

Bait is used to get a dog's attention and have him looking alert while showing. Different dogs are motivated by different foods. Try out a few different treat options until you find one that gets your dog's attention. Come to shows prepared with your dog's favorite treat. Some popular bait ideas are:

- **Liver treats.** Popular at dog shows. You can purchase these online or at shows or try baking them yourself. Here are some online recipes: www.sherob.com/info/cookbook/cb4.html, www.lowchensaustralia.com/bait.htm .

- **Cheese.** Small cheese cubes or string cheese works nicely.

- **Chicken.** Baked chicken is another favorite, also hot dogs (sliced and baked in the oven or cooked in the microwave).

- **Toys** can also be used for "bait" to keep your dog attentive and alert in the ring. Some handlers keep a small toy in their pocket along with liver for example.

If your show outfit doesn't have pockets, you might like to get a **bait bag.**

PERSONAL AND MISCELLANEOUS ITEMS

- **First Aid Kit:** one for your dog and one for yourself.
- **Doggie meds** (i.e., sometimes dogs get an upset tummy while traveling).
- **Your dog's ID tag, collar,** harness, and regular daily use leash.
- **Dog poop pickup bags.** Please dispose of these in the designated places at show sites and hotels.
- **Sewing kit:** to mend your outfit in a pinch. You may also want to bring a spare show outfit.
- **Some Cash:** for parking at events. Also, not all vendors take credit cards.
- **Folding chairs:** Seating is limited at most shows. Having your own chairs will be useful.
- **Shade covering** for sunny days: caps/umbrellas/tent. Also sunscreen.
- **Cooler** with water/snacks/sandwiches.
- **Paperwork:** show entry, judging schedule, directions to show, your dog's shot records, this record book …

DOG SHOW SHOPPING (Common show shopping sites where you can find most dog show gear.)

- The Show Dog Store: www.showdogstore.com/
- Cherrybrook: www.cherrybrook.com
- Chris Christensen: www.chrissystems.com/
- AKC Shop: www. shop.akc.org/
- 3 C's Dog: www.3cdog.net
- Best in Show Trolleys: www.bestinshowtrolleys.com/

- Total K-9 Connection: www.totalk9connection.com/
- Critter Beds: www.critterbeds.com
- Chewy: general pet shopping: www.chewy.com/
- PetEdge: www.petedge.com
- **Vendors at Dog Shows**

Pet Sitter Instruction Form

Print out this form for personal use when traveling to an event and needing a pet sitter.

DOG(S) NAME, DESCRIPTION, MICROCHIP

_____

_____

_____

_____

FEEDING SCHEDULE AND ROUTINE

MORNING FEEDING: _____

Medications/Supplements: _____

MIDDAY FEEDING: _____

Medications/Supplements: _____

EVENING FEEDING: _____

Medications/Supplements: _____

SPECIAL INSTRUCTIONS: _____

_____

_____

MY TRAVEL INFORMATION

Hotel/Location: _____

Contact Number: _____ Leaving/Returning on: _____

Emergency Contact Pet Sitter #2: _____

Primary Vet: _____**Emergency Vet:** _____

PET SITTING MEDICAL RELEASE FORM

I, _____ (pet owner) hereby give _____
(pet sitter's name) my express permission to take my pet(s) to the above-mentioned veterinarian (or to the closest open facility if the primary vet is not available). I give permission for the veterinarian to administer any care or medications necessary. I will assume full responsibility for the payment for any and all veterinary services provided.

Signed: _____ Date: _____

❀ ❀ My Dog Grooming Goal Calendar ❀ ❀

Print out this page to resuse monthly. Set your monthly dog show grooming goals. Write your dog's name, what you plan to do (i.e. bath, nails), and any concerns. Include grooming products used for future reference.

MONTH:

SUN	MON	TUES	WED	THU	FRID	SAT

MY DOG SHOW GROOMING GOAL CALENDAR

B-Bath   BR-Brush   N-Nails   C-Clip   E-Ears   T-Teeth   AG-Anal Glands

❧ ❧ Recommended Reading & Links ❧ ❧

CONFORMATION (WEBSITES)

- **Visit AKC.org and type in the search bar the following articles:**

  Get Started in Conformation Dog Shows

  A Beginner's Guide to Dog Shows

  AKC Show Manual

  Conformation Show Resources

- Youtube: Type in the search bar "conformation training for dogs." There are some excellent tutorial videos demonstrating stacking your dog, gaiting patterns, and more.

CONFORMATION (BOOKS)

- *The New Complete Dog Book,* 22nd Edition, by the American Kennel Club: A comprehensive glossary of dog-related terms, as well as pictures, histories, and standards of all AKC recognized breeds.

- *K-9 Structure & Terminology*, by Edward M. Gilbert, Jr. and Thelma R. Brown.

- *The Dog in Action:* A Study of Anatomy and Locomotion as Applying to all Breeds, by McDowell Lyon.

- *Born To Win: Breed To Succeed,* 2nd Edition, by Patricia Craige Trotter. It explores every facet of breeding and exhibiting top winning Pure Bred Dogs.

- Log on to Amazon for more options. Search, "Dog Show Training Books." Reviews will help you choose.

CONFORMATION (MAGAZINES)

- *AKC Gazette:* www.akc.org/products-services/magazines/akc-gazette/: Published monthly (online only). It has articles on canine health, behavior and events; columns on specific breeds; and an Events Calendar.

- *Canine Chronicle:* www.caninechronicle.com/

- *Showsight:* www.showsightmagazine.com/ A place for purebred dogs with purpose.

- *Dogs in Review:* @DogsInReview, a magazine for the sport of purebred dogs around the world.

- *Dog News:* www.dognews.com/

ASSOCIATIONS

- AKC Registered Handlers Directory: www.apps.akc.org/apps/handlers/handlersprogram_directory.cfm

- Professional Handlers Association (PHA): (301) 924-0089, www.phadoghandlers.com/

- Owner Handlers Association (OHA): (914) 374-2708 @ownerhandlersassoc

KENNEL CLUBS

The major, most widely accepted kennel clubs for English-speaking countries are:

- AKC: The American Kennel Club: www.akc.org (United States of America)
- UKC: The United Kennel Club: www.ukcdogs.com/ (United States of America)
- Canadian Kennel Club www.ckc.ca/en (Canada)
- The Kennel Club www.thekennelclub.org/uk (United Kingdom)
- FCI: The Fédération Cynologique Internationale (World Canine Organization) www.fci.be/en/
- Australian National Kennel Council www.ankc.org.au
- East Africa Kennel Club (Kenya) www.eastafricakennelclub.com
- Kennel Club of India www.indiakennels.com
- New Zealand Kennel Club www.nzkc.org.nz
- Kennel Union of Southern Africa www.kusa.co.za

MORE LEARNING OPPORTUNITIES

- Handling Classes: To find a handling class near you visit www.akc.org/clubs-delegates/
- Seminars and Conferences: Online event organizer of dog-related seminars www.puppyworks.com
- AKC S.T.A.R. Puppy: Exciting program designed to get dog owners and their puppies off to a good start. Visit AKC.org and type in the search bar: "AKC Star Puppy"
- Canine Good Citizen (C.G.C.): Open to all dogs—purebred and mixed breed. The C.G.C. title is a great introduction to all dog sports and activities. Visit AKC.org, type "CGC" in search bar to learn more.
- Fear Free Pets: www.fearfreepets.com/about/what-is-fear-free/

OTHER CANINE SPORTING EVENTS

- **Visit AKC.org and type in the search bar:**

  Get Started in Dog Sports and Events (agility, obedience, tracking, etc.)

  AKC National Owner Handled Series

  Junior Showmanship

  AKC Purebred Alternative Registry (PAL)

  AKC Canine Partners for Mixed Breeds

  AKC's Official Canine Ambassador Program

  AKC Titles & Programs You Can Do From Home

- UKC Performance Listing: www.ukcdogs.com/performance-listing
- IABCA International All Breed Canine Association Events: www.iabca.com/index.html

TRAVELING TO AN EVENT? PET TRAVEL SUPPORT

- Pet Travel Hotline, 1-800-545-USDA

- Pet Airways, (888) 738-2479, PetAirways.com

- Pet Travel Information, (877) 241-0184

- PetTravel.com, Wordlwide resource for pet travel and pet-friendly hotels.

- **Visit AKC.org and type in the search bar:**

  Flying With a Dog? Tips for Traveling Safely

  The Complete Guide to Traveling With Your Dog

CANINE HEALTH

- PetPoisonHelpline.com: (855) 764-7661

- ASPCA Animal Poison Control Center: (888) 426-4435

- AKC Canine Health Foundation (AKC CHF): www.akcchf.org/

- Orthopedic Foundation for Animals (OFA) https://ofa.org/

- Canine Health Information Center (CHIC): www.caninehealthinfo.org/

- American Veterinary Medical Association: AVMA.org

- American Holistic Veterinary Medical Association: AHVMA.org

- **Visit AKC.org and type in the search bar:**

  Canine Health

  Breed Health Testing Requirements

  AKC Breeder Of Merit Program

  AKC Bred with H.E.A.R.T. Program

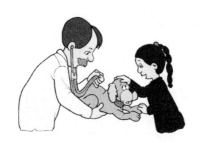

BREED HEALTH TESTING CLINICS

Take advantage of health testing clinics offered at dog shows. These will be listed in your premium list.

You may need to pre-register to secure a time slot and mail in a fee.

Record these in your dog show log with the time you are scheduled for.

Dog Show Safety Tips

- Never leave a dog unattended in a closed car or direct sunlight during hot weather. The temperature inside a vehicle is significantly higher than outside, placing a dog at risk for heatstroke or possible death.

- Strenuous exercise during extremely hot days is not without risk. Ensure dogs are properly hydrated for their sports event and resting in the shade when possible. Use crate fans, cooling mats, or an all-weather SPACE blanket if needed to keep your dog cool. Don't hesitate to withdraw your dog from an event if they appear uncomfortable or ill.

- Wherever possible, always avoid leaving dogs unattended in a car or R.V. But if for any reason they must be left for a short while (weather permitting), leave the car parked in a safe and shaded place. Also, leave the air conditioning running or the windows partially open and crate fans on to ensure proper airflow, lock doors to prevent dog theft, and be sure your dog has access to fresh water.

- Ask someone to watch your crates if you need to be absent for a moment, and/or barricade or lock crates to prevent someone from accidentally letting your dog loose.

- Be aware that leaving unattended dogs on grooming tables or in pens is not without risk (i.e. falling off)..

- Be watchful that your dog doesn't snatch food from the floor or grassy areas while you are walking around together. Also, when setting up outdoors, check the grounds for foreign objects or food. There could be leftover rotting bait that's infested with bugs.

- Please pick up after your dog. Have plastic bags handy to remove dogs' waste, and paper towels to wipe up any accidents indoors. Certain canine diseases can spread through fecal contact on shoes.

- Be aware of canine disease (i.e., Parvovirus) and take precautionary measures to prevent its spread. Remove and disinfect shoes and clothes when traveling to and from dog shows and other canine sports events. Keep your dog current on vaccines. Bring your dogs' health and vaccine records with you.

- Make sure dogs have proper identification while traveling (i.e., Collar and I.D. tag, tattoo, microchip). Collars may be removed while dogs are crated to prevent a choking hazard.

- Be aware of other dogs at the showgrounds. For example, if you're pulling a show trolley with crates, be careful not to run over a dog's paw or tail while a dog is sitting ringside.

- If your show girl is in heat, try to keep her at a distance from male dogs. You can also inform exhibitors nearby so they can be aware while in the ring.

- Last but not least, your safety is a priority too. Consider things like proper hydration on hot days, sunscreen, road safety while traveling to and from shows, etc.

Canine Sports remind us
that **DOGS** aren't just our
best friends: they're our
tireless teammates, joining us
in the exhilarating pursuit of
Triumph, Joy, and Sportsmanship!

~ Leila Grandemange

Part 5

Dog Show Address Book

Record names of judges you've shown to and the dogs presented,
along with other dog show related contacts—handlers, etc.

Money can buy you a fine dog, but
only love can make him wag his tail.

—Kinky Friedman

Dog Show Judge Log & Contacts

Record the judges you've shown to and the dogs presented. *Score* for future reference.
Log handlers, trainers, groomers, or other important dog show contacts.

NAME_____ ☺ ☺ ☹ Email_____
Address_____Phone_____
Dogs Presented_____

NAME_____ ☺ ☺ ☹ Email_____
Address_____Phone_____
Dogs Presented_____

NAME_____ ☺ ☺ ☹ Email_____
Address_____Phone_____
Dogs Presented_____

NAME_____ ☺ ☺ ☹ Email_____
Address_____Phone_____
Dogs Presented_____

NAME_____ ☺ ☺ ☹ Email_____
Address_____Phone_____
Dogs Presented_____

NAME_____ ☺ ☺ ☹ Email_____
Address_____Phone_____
Dogs Presented_____

NAME_____ ☺ ☺ ☹ Email_____
Address_____Phone_____
Dogs Presented_____

NAME_____ ☺ ☺ ☹ Email_____
Address_____Phone_____
Dogs Presented_____

NAME_____ ☺ ☺ ☹ Email_____
Address_____Phone_____
Dogs Presented_____

Dog Show Judge Log & Contacts

B

NAME_____ ☺ ☺ ☹ _Email_____
Address_____Phone_____
Dogs Presented_____

NAME_____ ☺ ☺ ☹ _Email_____
Address_____Phone_____
Dogs Presented_____

NAME_____ ☺ ☺ ☹ _Email_____
Address_____Phone_____
Dogs Presented_____

NAME_____ ☺ ☺ ☹ _Email_____
Address_____Phone_____
Dogs Presented_____

NAME_____ ☺ ☺ ☹ _Email_____
Address_____Phone_____
Dogs Presented_____

NAME_____ ☺ ☺ ☹ _Email_____
Address_____Phone_____
Dogs Presented_____

NAME_____ ☺ ☺ ☹ _Email_____
Address_____Phone_____
Dogs Presented_____

NAME_____ ☺ ☺ ☹ _Email_____
Address_____Phone_____
Dogs Presented_____

NAME_____ ☺ ☺ ☹ _Email_____
Address_____Phone_____
Dogs Presented_____

Dog Show Judge Log & Contacts

Record the judges you've shown to and the dogs presented. *Score* for future reference.
Log handlers, trainers, groomers, or other important dog show contacts.

NAME_____ ☺ ☺ ☹ _Email_____
Address_____Phone_____
Dogs Presented_____

NAME_____ ☺ ☺ ☹ _Email_____
Address_____Phone_____
Dogs Presented_____

NAME_____ ☺ ☺ ☹ _Email_____
Address_____Phone_____
Dogs Presented_____

NAME_____ ☺ ☺ ☹ _Email_____
Address_____Phone_____
Dogs Presented_____

NAME_____ ☺ ☺ ☹ _Email_____
Address_____Phone_____
Dogs Presented_____

NAME_____ ☺ ☺ ☹ _Email_____
Address_____Phone_____
Dogs Presented_____

NAME_____ ☺ ☺ ☹ _Email_____
Address_____Phone_____
Dogs Presented_____

NAME_____ ☺ ☺ ☹ _Email_____
Address_____Phone_____
Dogs Presented_____

NAME_____ ☺ ☺ ☹ _Email_____
Address_____Phone_____
Dogs Presented_____

Dog Show Judge Log & Contacts

D

NAME_____ ☺ ☻ ☹ _Email_____
Address_____Phone_____
Dogs Presented_____

NAME_____ ☺ ☻ ☹ _Email_____
Address_____Phone_____
Dogs Presented_____

NAME_____ ☺ ☻ ☹ _Email_____
Address_____Phone_____
Dogs Presented_____

NAME_____ ☺ ☻ ☹ _Email_____
Address_____Phone_____
Dogs Presented_____

NAME_____ ☺ ☻ ☹ _Email_____
Address_____Phone_____
Dogs Presented_____

NAME_____ ☺ ☻ ☹ _Email_____
Address_____Phone_____
Dogs Presented_____

NAME_____ ☺ ☻ ☹ _Email_____
Address_____Phone_____
Dogs Presented_____

NAME_____ ☺ ☻ ☹ _Email_____
Address_____Phone_____
Dogs Presented_____

NAME_____ ☺ ☻ ☹ _Email_____
Address_____Phone_____
Dogs Presented_____

Dog Show Judge Log & Contacts

Record the judges you've shown to and the dogs presented. *Score* for future reference.
Log handlers, trainers, groomers, or other important dog show contacts.

NAME_____ ☺ 😐 ☹ Email_____
Address_____Phone_____
Dogs Presented_____

NAME_____ ☺ 😐 ☹ Email_____
Address_____Phone_____
Dogs Presented_____

NAME_____ ☺ 😐 ☹ Email_____
Address_____Phone_____
Dogs Presented_____

NAME_____ ☺ 😐 ☹ Email_____
Address_____Phone_____
Dogs Presented_____

NAME_____ ☺ 😐 ☹ Email_____
Address_____Phone_____
Dogs Presented_____

NAME_____ ☺ 😐 ☹ Email_____
Address_____Phone_____
Dogs Presented_____

NAME_____ ☺ 😐 ☹ Email_____
Address_____Phone_____
Dogs Presented_____

NAME_____ ☺ 😐 ☹ Email_____
Address_____Phone_____
Dogs Presented_____

NAME_____ ☺ 😐 ☹ Email_____
Address_____Phone_____
Dogs Presented_____

Dog Show Judge Log & Contacts

NAME_____ ☺ ☹ ☹ _Email_____
Address_____Phone_____
Dogs Presented_____

NAME_____ ☺ ☹ ☹ _Email_____
Address_____Phone_____
Dogs Presented_____

NAME_____ ☺ ☹ ☹ _Email_____
Address_____Phone_____
Dogs Presented_____

NAME_____ ☺ ☹ ☹ _Email_____
Address_____Phone_____
Dogs Presented_____

NAME_____ ☺ ☹ ☹ _Email_____
Address_____Phone_____
Dogs Presented_____

NAME_____ ☺ ☹ ☹ _Email_____
Address_____Phone_____
Dogs Presented_____

NAME_____ ☺ ☹ ☹ _Email_____
Address_____Phone_____
Dogs Presented_____

NAME_____ ☺ ☹ ☹ _Email_____
Address_____Phone_____
Dogs Presented_____

NAME_____ ☺ ☹ ☹ _Email_____
Address_____Phone_____
Dogs Presented_____

Dog Show Judge Log & Contacts

Record the judges you've shown to and the dogs presented. *Score* for future reference.
Log handlers, trainers, groomers, or other important dog show contacts.

NAME_____ ☺ ☹ ☹ Email_____
Address_____Phone_____
Dogs Presented_____

NAME_____ ☺ ☹ ☹ Email_____
Address_____Phone_____
Dogs Presented_____

NAME_____ ☺ ☹ ☹ Email_____
Address_____Phone_____
Dogs Presented_____

NAME_____ ☺ ☹ ☹ Email_____
Address_____Phone_____
Dogs Presented_____

NAME_____ ☺ ☹ ☹ Email_____
Address_____Phone_____
Dogs Presented_____

NAME_____ ☺ ☹ ☹ Email_____
Address_____Phone_____
Dogs Presented_____

NAME_____ ☺ ☹ ☹ Email_____
Address_____Phone_____
Dogs Presented_____

NAME_____ ☺ ☹ ☹ Email_____
Address_____Phone_____
Dogs Presented_____

NAME_____ ☺ ☹ ☹ Email_____
Address_____Phone_____
Dogs Presented_____

Dog Show Judge Log & Contacts

NAME_____ ☺ ☺ ☹ _Email_____
Address_____Phone_____
Dogs Presented_____

NAME_____ ☺ ☺ ☹ _Email_____
Address_____Phone_____
Dogs Presented_____

NAME_____ ☺ ☺ ☹ _Email_____
Address_____Phone_____
Dogs Presented_____

NAME_____ ☺ ☺ ☹ _Email_____
Address_____Phone_____
Dogs Presented_____

NAME_____ ☺ ☺ ☹ _Email_____
Address_____Phone_____
Dogs Presented_____

NAME_____ ☺ ☺ ☹ _Email_____
Address_____Phone_____
Dogs Presented_____

NAME_____ ☺ ☺ ☹ _Email_____
Address_____Phone_____
Dogs Presented_____

NAME_____ ☺ ☺ ☹ _Email_____
Address_____Phone_____
Dogs Presented_____

NAME_____ ☺ ☺ ☹ _Email_____
Address_____Phone_____
Dogs Presented_____

Dog Show Judge Log & Contacts

Record the judges you've shown to and the dogs presented. *Score* for future reference.
Log handlers, trainers, groomers, or other important dog show contacts.

NAME_____ ☺ 😐 ☹ _Email_____
Address_____Phone_____
Dogs Presented_____

NAME_____ ☺ 😐 ☹ _Email_____
Address_____Phone_____
Dogs Presented_____

NAME_____ ☺ 😐 ☹ _Email_____
Address_____Phone_____
Dogs Presented_____

NAME_____ ☺ 😐 ☹ _Email_____
Address_____Phone_____
Dogs Presented_____

NAME_____ ☺ 😐 ☹ _Email_____
Address_____Phone_____
Dogs Presented_____

NAME_____ ☺ 😐 ☹ _Email_____
Address_____Phone_____
Dogs Presented_____

NAME_____ ☺ 😐 ☹ _Email_____
Address_____Phone_____
Dogs Presented_____

NAME_____ ☺ 😐 ☹ _Email_____
Address_____Phone_____
Dogs Presented_____

NAME_____ ☺ 😐 ☹ _Email_____
Address_____Phone_____
Dogs Presented_____

Dog Show Judge Log & Contacts

J

NAME_____ ☺ ☺ ☹ _Email_____
Address_____Phone_____
Dogs Presented_____

NAME_____ ☺ ☺ ☹ _Email_____
Address_____Phone_____
Dogs Presented_____

NAME_____ ☺ ☺ ☹ _Email_____
Address_____Phone_____
Dogs Presented_____

NAME_____ ☺ ☺ ☹ _Email_____
Address_____Phone_____
Dogs Presented_____

NAME_____ ☺ ☺ ☹ _Email_____
Address_____Phone_____
Dogs Presented_____

NAME_____ ☺ ☺ ☹ _Email_____
Address_____Phone_____
Dogs Presented_____

NAME_____ ☺ ☺ ☹ _Email_____
Address_____Phone_____
Dogs Presented_____

NAME_____ ☺ ☺ ☹ _Email_____
Address_____Phone_____
Dogs Presented_____

NAME_____ ☺ ☺ ☹ _Email_____
Address_____Phone_____
Dogs Presented_____

Dog Show Judge Log & Contacts

Record the judges you've shown to and the dogs presented. *Score* for future reference.
Log handlers, trainers, groomers, or other important dog show contacts.

NAME_____ ☺ ☺ ☹ _Email_____

Address_____Phone_____

Dogs Presented_____

NAME_____ ☺ ☺ ☹ _Email_____

Address_____Phone_____

Dogs Presented_____

NAME_____ ☺ ☺ ☹ _Email_____

Address_____Phone_____

Dogs Presented_____

NAME_____ ☺ ☺ ☹ _Email_____

Address_____Phone_____

Dogs Presented_____

NAME_____ ☺ ☺ ☹ _Email_____

Address_____Phone_____

Dogs Presented_____

NAME_____ ☺ ☺ ☹ _Email_____

Address_____Phone_____

Dogs Presented_____

NAME_____ ☺ ☺ ☹ _Email_____

Address_____Phone_____

Dogs Presented_____

NAME_____ ☺ ☺ ☹ _Email_____

Address_____Phone_____

Dogs Presented_____

NAME_____ ☺ ☺ ☹ _Email_____

Address_____Phone_____

Dogs Presented_____

Dog Show Judge Log & Contacts

NAME_____ ☺ ☺ ☹ _Email_____
Address_____Phone_____
Dogs Presented_____

NAME_____ ☺ ☺ ☹ _Email_____
Address_____Phone_____
Dogs Presented_____

NAME_____ ☺ ☺ ☹ _Email_____
Address_____Phone_____
Dogs Presented_____

NAME_____ ☺ ☺ ☹ _Email_____
Address_____Phone_____
Dogs Presented_____

NAME_____ ☺ ☺ ☹ _Email_____
Address_____Phone_____
Dogs Presented_____

NAME_____ ☺ ☺ ☹ _Email_____
Address_____Phone_____
Dogs Presented_____

NAME_____ ☺ ☺ ☹ _Email_____
Address_____Phone_____
Dogs Presented_____

NAME_____ ☺ ☺ ☹ _Email_____
Address_____Phone_____
Dogs Presented_____

NAME_____ ☺ ☺ ☹ _Email_____
Address_____Phone_____
Dogs Presented_____

Dog Show Judge Log & Contacts

Record the judges you've shown to and the dogs presented. *Score* for future reference.
Log handlers, trainers, groomers, or other important dog show contacts.

NAME_____ ☺ ☺ ☹ Email_____
Address_____Phone_____
Dogs Presented_____

NAME_____ ☺ ☺ ☹ Email_____
Address_____Phone_____
Dogs Presented_____

NAME_____ ☺ ☺ ☹ Email_____
Address_____Phone_____
Dogs Presented_____

NAME_____ ☺ ☺ ☹ Email_____
Address_____Phone_____
Dogs Presented_____

NAME_____ ☺ ☺ ☹ Email_____
Address_____Phone_____
Dogs Presented_____

NAME_____ ☺ ☺ ☹ Email_____
Address_____Phone_____
Dogs Presented_____

NAME_____ ☺ ☺ ☹ Email_____
Address_____Phone_____
Dogs Presented_____

NAME_____ ☺ ☺ ☹ Email_____
Address_____Phone_____
Dogs Presented_____

NAME_____ ☺ ☺ ☹ Email_____
Address_____Phone_____
Dogs Presented_____

Dog Show Judge Log & Contacts

NAME_____ ☺ ☺ ☹ _Email_____
Address_____Phone_____
Dogs Presented_____

NAME_____ ☺ ☺ ☹ _Email_____
Address_____Phone_____
Dogs Presented_____

NAME_____ ☺ ☺ ☹ _Email_____
Address_____Phone_____
Dogs Presented_____

NAME_____ ☺ ☺ ☹ _Email_____
Address_____Phone_____
Dogs Presented_____

NAME_____ ☺ ☺ ☹ _Email_____
Address_____Phone_____
Dogs Presented_____

NAME_____ ☺ ☺ ☹ _Email_____
Address_____Phone_____
Dogs Presented_____

NAME_____ ☺ ☺ ☹ _Email_____
Address_____Phone_____
Dogs Presented_____

NAME_____ ☺ ☺ ☹ _Email_____
Address_____Phone_____
Dogs Presented_____

NAME_____ ☺ ☺ ☹ _Email_____
Address_____Phone_____
Dogs Presented_____

Dog Show Judge Log & Contacts

Record the judges you've shown to and the dogs presented. *Score* for future reference.
Log handlers, trainers, groomers, or other important dog show contacts.

NAME_____ ☺ 😐 ☹ Email_____
Address_____Phone_____
Dogs Presented_____

NAME_____ ☺ 😐 ☹ Email_____
Address_____Phone_____
Dogs Presented_____

NAME_____ ☺ 😐 ☹ Email_____
Address_____Phone_____
Dogs Presented_____

NAME_____ ☺ 😐 ☹ Email_____
Address_____Phone_____
Dogs Presented_____

NAME_____ ☺ 😐 ☹ Email_____
Address_____Phone_____
Dogs Presented_____

NAME_____ ☺ 😐 ☹ Email_____
Address_____Phone_____
Dogs Presented_____

NAME_____ ☺ 😐 ☹ Email_____
Address_____Phone_____
Dogs Presented_____

NAME_____ ☺ 😐 ☹ Email_____
Address_____Phone_____
Dogs Presented_____

NAME_____ ☺ 😐 ☹ Email_____
Address_____Phone_____
Dogs Presented_____

Dog Show Judge Log & Contacts

P

NAME_____ ☺ ☺ ☹ Email_____
Address_____Phone_____
Dogs Presented_____

NAME_____ ☺ ☺ ☹ Email_____
Address_____Phone_____
Dogs Presented_____

NAME_____ ☺ ☺ ☹ Email_____
Address_____Phone_____
Dogs Presented_____

NAME_____ ☺ ☺ ☹ Email_____
Address_____Phone_____
Dogs Presented_____

NAME_____ ☺ ☺ ☹ Email_____
Address_____Phone_____
Dogs Presented_____

NAME_____ ☺ ☺ ☹ Email_____
Address_____Phone_____
Dogs Presented_____

NAME_____ ☺ ☺ ☹ Email_____
Address_____Phone_____
Dogs Presented_____

NAME_____ ☺ ☺ ☹ Email_____
Address_____Phone_____
Dogs Presented_____

NAME_____ ☺ ☺ ☹ Email_____
Address_____Phone_____
Dogs Presented_____

Dog Show Judge Log & Contacts

Record the judges you've shown to and the dogs presented. *Score* for future reference.
Log handlers, trainers, groomers, or other important dog show contacts.

NAME_____ ☺ ☺ ☹ _Email_____
Address_____Phone_____
Dogs Presented_____

NAME_____ ☺ ☺ ☹ _Email_____
Address_____Phone_____
Dogs Presented_____

NAME_____ ☺ ☺ ☹ _Email_____
Address_____Phone_____
Dogs Presented_____

NAME_____ ☺ ☺ ☹ _Email_____
Address_____Phone_____
Dogs Presented_____

NAME_____ ☺ ☺ ☹ _Email_____
Address_____Phone_____
Dogs Presented_____

NAME_____ ☺ ☺ ☹ _Email_____
Address_____Phone_____
Dogs Presented_____

NAME_____ ☺ ☺ ☹ _Email_____
Address_____Phone_____
Dogs Presented_____

NAME_____ ☺ ☺ ☹ _Email_____
Address_____Phone_____
Dogs Presented_____

NAME_____ ☺ ☺ ☹ _Email_____
Address_____Phone_____
Dogs Presented_____

Dog Show Judge Log & Contacts

NAME_____ ☺ ☺ ☹ _Email_____
Address_____Phone_____
Dogs Presented_____

NAME_____ ☺ ☺ ☹ _Email_____
Address_____Phone_____
Dogs Presented_____

NAME_____ ☺ ☺ ☹ _Email_____
Address_____Phone_____
Dogs Presented_____

NAME_____ ☺ ☺ ☹ _Email_____
Address_____Phone_____
Dogs Presented_____

NAME_____ ☺ ☺ ☹ _Email_____
Address_____Phone_____
Dogs Presented_____

NAME_____ ☺ ☺ ☹ _Email_____
Address_____Phone_____
Dogs Presented_____

NAME_____ ☺ ☺ ☹ _Email_____
Address_____Phone_____
Dogs Presented_____

NAME_____ ☺ ☺ ☹ _Email_____
Address_____Phone_____
Dogs Presented_____

NAME_____ ☺ ☺ ☹ _Email_____
Address_____Phone_____
Dogs Presented_____

Record the judges you've shown to and the dogs presented. *Score* for future reference.
Log handlers, trainers, groomers, or other important dog show contacts.

NAME_____ ☺ ☹ ☹ _Email_____
Address_____Phone_____
Dogs Presented_____

NAME_____ ☺ ☹ ☹ _Email_____
Address_____Phone_____
Dogs Presented_____

NAME_____ ☺ ☹ ☹ _Email_____
Address_____Phone_____
Dogs Presented_____

NAME_____ ☺ ☹ ☹ _Email_____
Address_____Phone_____
Dogs Presented_____

NAME_____ ☺ ☹ ☹ _Email_____
Address_____Phone_____
Dogs Presented_____

NAME_____ ☺ ☹ ☹ _Email_____
Address_____Phone_____
Dogs Presented_____

NAME_____ ☺ ☹ ☹ _Email_____
Address_____Phone_____
Dogs Presented_____

NAME_____ ☺ ☹ ☹ _Email_____
Address_____Phone_____
Dogs Presented_____

NAME_____ ☺ ☹ ☹ _Email_____
Address_____Phone_____
Dogs Presented_____

Dog Show Judge Log & Contacts

NAME_____ ☺ ☹ ☹ Email_____
Address_____ Phone_____
Dogs Presented_____

NAME_____ ☺ ☹ ☹ Email_____
Address_____ Phone_____
Dogs Presented_____

NAME_____ ☺ ☹ ☹ Email_____
Address_____ Phone_____
Dogs Presented_____

NAME_____ ☺ ☹ ☹ Email_____
Address_____ Phone_____
Dogs Presented_____

NAME_____ ☺ ☹ ☹ Email_____
Address_____ Phone_____
Dogs Presented_____

NAME_____ ☺ ☹ ☹ Email_____
Address_____ Phone_____
Dogs Presented_____

NAME_____ ☺ ☹ ☹ Email_____
Address_____ Phone_____
Dogs Presented_____

NAME_____ ☺ ☹ ☹ Email_____
Address_____ Phone_____
Dogs Presented_____

NAME_____ ☺ ☹ ☹ Email_____
Address_____ Phone_____
Dogs Presented_____

Dog Show Judge Log & Contacts

Record the judges you've shown to and the dogs presented. *Score* for future reference.
Log handlers, trainers, groomers, or other important dog show contacts.

NAME_____ ☺ ☺ ☹ _Email_____
Address_____Phone_____
Dogs Presented_____

NAME_____ ☺ ☺ ☹ _Email_____
Address_____Phone_____
Dogs Presented_____

NAME_____ ☺ ☺ ☹ _Email_____
Address_____Phone_____
Dogs Presented_____

NAME_____ ☺ ☺ ☹ _Email_____
Address_____Phone_____
Dogs Presented_____

NAME_____ ☺ ☺ ☹ _Email_____
Address_____Phone_____
Dogs Presented_____

NAME_____ ☺ ☺ ☹ _Email_____
Address_____Phone_____
Dogs Presented_____

NAME_____ ☺ ☺ ☹ _Email_____
Address_____Phone_____
Dogs Presented_____

NAME_____ ☺ ☺ ☹ _Email_____
Address_____Phone_____
Dogs Presented_____

NAME_____ ☺ ☺ ☹ _Email_____
Address_____Phone_____
Dogs Presented_____

Dog Show Judge Log & Contacts

Y-Z

NAME_____Email_____

Address_____Phone_____

Dogs Presented_____

NAME_____Email_____

Address_____Phone_____

Dogs Presented_____

NAME_____Email_____

Address_____Phone_____

Dogs Presented_____

NAME_____Email_____

Address_____Phone_____

Dogs Presented_____

Emergency Numbers at a Glance

NAME_____Email_____

Address_____Phone_____

NAME_____Email_____

Address_____Phone_____

NAME_____Email_____

Address_____Phone_____

NAME_____Email_____

Address_____Phone_____

NAME_____Email_____

Address_____Phone_____

NAME_____Email_____

Address_____Phone_____

Best in Show

Congratulations, you did it!

BEST IN SHOW

It takes a village!

Notes

And the journey goes on . . .

Acknowledgments

MY SINCERE THANKS to The American Kennel Club for the wealth of information provided at www.akc.org, to breed experts James G. Reynolds and Dennis Homes for sharing their time and expertise, to my parents and dear friend MaryAnn Edman for help with editing, to my family for their love and support, and to God who makes all things possible!

THANK YOU ALSO TO THE FOLLOWING CONTRIBUTORS:

Page 150, Dennis Homes, "History of Dog Shows."

Pages 170-171, Laura Reeves, "How to Count Championship Points."

Page 177, Dog parts diagram FCI Federation Cynologique Internationale.

COVER AND INTERIOR DESIGN, Leila Grandemange, Sunnyville Publishing

PHOTO CREDITS:

All photos by Leila Grandemange, of her and her family and Cavalier King Charles Spaniel show dogs, except as noted below.

P. 9 Ibizan Hounds at Dog Show; p.41 dog show MorgueFile.com; p. 151 The 142nd Westminster KC BIS dog being examined by judge; p.153 Wire Fox Terrier BIS with cup; p.167 Shelly Fields Photography Studio, Rachel Venier and her dog Devon; p.172 boxer: Maura McIntosh and her dog Keeva; p.175 German Shepherd freepic.diller; p.180 Ruperon Shepherds, Ruth Fisher; p.187 Welsh Corgi by Master1305 Freepik; p.189 Australian Shepherd at Crufts Dog Show, Melissa Keiser, Unsplash; p.191 The 139th Westminster KC BIS Hound 15" with handler William Alexandre.

Please leave an online book review
and let others know what you thought.

FOLLOW LEILA ON HER AMAZON AUTHOR PAGE
to be notified about her latest books. Or Subscribe to
her website at www.LeilaGrandemange.com

Printed in Great Britain
by Amazon

33831150R00123